DISASTER

Another Barclay House Book
by
Troy Allen
GANG WARS OF THE 20'S

DISASTER

by Troy Allen

CASTLE BOOKS / NEW JERSEY

CONTENTS

INTRODUCTION

The most destructive period in the history of the United States, according to Red Cross figures, was the decade of the 1950s, during which over 3,000 natural disasters left 1,600,000 people permanently or temporarily displaced by an unprecedented series of natural events. Throughout recorded history, the figures of loss from catastrophe and catacylsm of nature are staggering.

In the first sixty years of the twentieth century, hurricanes have taken 17,000 American lives and caused property damage of five billion dollars. There is a statistical probability that once every twelve years there will be a hurricane so violent that 100 lives will be lost and damage will be as much as a billion dollars. In other countries, loss of life from hurricanes has been even greater than that in the United States. There are an average of thirty-six hurricanes a year, and even modern hurricane warning systems do not save many people who have no time to flee or who are caught in the act of escape and hurled to destruction.

Tornadoes kill about 200 people each year in the United States and the injury rate is about thirteen times greater than the death rate. Property damage from tornadoes is about 15 million dollars a year. Throughout the world, about 150 people are killed every year in avalanches.

World losses from floods, both in lives and in property damage, are tremendous. The most lethal flood in recorded history occurred in September and October of 1887, when the Hwang Ho River rose above its 70-foot levees. In that one flood alone, 900,000 people were killed, two million people were left homeless, and 300 villages were swept completely away.

There are over a million earthquakes each year —about one every two minutes. Most of them are extremely slight; about 20 are serious but occur in uninhabited areas; and about five each year are killers. One of the greatest killer earthquakes of all time occurred in China in the sixteenth century, wiping out more than 800,000 people in an afternoon.

Erupting volcanoes are the greatest spectacle in nature, and for those who are close enough to observe, are often deadly. Since the turn of the sixteenth century, volcanoes have claimed more than 200,000 lives. The eruption of Krakatoa in 1883, with its subsequent seismic sea wave, was probably one of the greatest disasters the world has ever witnessed. Thirty-six thousand people were killed, and almost 300 villages and towns were inundated before the disturbance on the waters died down.

Since the dawn of time, violent and relentless natural forces have been altering and shifting the course of events on earth. Changes in weather have altered the landscape, drying swamps into deserts, flooding ancient canyons and shaping and reshaping the edges of the great continents. The retreat and advance of the gigantic polar ice packs has changed the climate so completely that whole genera and species of animals have become extinct, leaving an open field for a new race that eventually would become man.

When men began to proliferate, they too began to experience the assault of the elements, and to be influenced by earthshaking events beneath the crust of the land and beneath the sea.

Time and again, natural forces have changed the course of human history. In the winter of 1777, General Washington relied on extremes of cold at Princeton to freeze muddy roads so that he could bring artillery within range of Cornwallis. What if the weather had been mild that year?

Centuries later, in the middle of World War II, a modern battle fleet was helpless in the grip of a gigantic typhoon in the Pacific. Task Force 38 of the United States Third Fleet was in the midst of refueling when the typhoon headed toward it off the Philippines on December 17-18, 1944, and many of the ships were low in ballast and unable to fight the storm. In the typhoon, the fleet lost three destroyers, 146 aircraft and 790 men. Eighteen other ships suffered major damage, and so many others needed repair that the course of the war in the Pacific was altered while the fleet recovered. Again, on June 5, 1945, the Third Fleet was struck by a typhoon as it was battling for Okinawa in the Northwest Pacific.

As a result of these two typhoons, improvements were made in ship design, and the U.S. Navy began to study the possibility of actually steering typhoons toward an enemy fleet.

This is only one example of man's irresistible impulse to harness the unimaginable forces of nature for his own benefit. The results of Franklin's research on lightning have completely transformed the modern world; research on the prediction of earthquakes has yielded precious knowledge of the earth's interior. Also as a result of earthquake research, we now have a widely practiced method of locating valuable minerals beneath the earth's surface by studying the waves which result from a dynamite charge.

Geothermal heat, one of the most important products of volcanism, has been used for centuries as a source of energy in a small way. With today's energy crisis, it is not unlikely that methods will be found to put to use the full potential of geothermal energy. The United States, Italy,

10

New Zealand, Iceland, Russia and Japan all have geothermal power plants in operation now.

However, harnessing geothermal heat and other forms of energy released by natural phenomena is in the future for man. At present, the energy, in gigantic amounts, is confined to its natural outlets. Some idea of the amounts of energy released by earthquakes, volcanic eruption, and tornadoes is given by a selection of comparisons from John Harpum's energy scale in *The Elements Rage*. A magnitude 4 earthquake, about halfway up the Richter scale, exceeds the kinetic energy of a 312,000 lb. jet aircraft flying at 600 mph. The energy of a one-ton space vehicle orbiting the earth is exceeded by both the kinetic energy of the rotation of a tornado and the kinetic energy of a one-half-million ton avalanche.

The energy released in the Mt. Pelée eruption in 1902 far exceeded the energy of the fission bomb that destroyed Hiroshima. The highest magnitude earthquake on the Richter scale exceeds the energy of a 100-megaton fusion bomb, and the energy released in the Krakatoa eruption in 1883 exceeded even that of the greatest earthquake ever recorded.

The total annual release of earthquake energy alone at the present epoch is in excess of both the 100-megaton fusion bomb and the total annual food energy requirements of the entire human race.

After a few of these comparisons, it is impossible to escape the conclusion that man, even at his most destructive, is puny on any scale in which the energies of natural phenomena are included. The destruction at Hiroshima has stood as a yardstick for the power unleashed by men, but it seems small in relation to the fantastic power of the elements. When natural energies are turned upon man and his works, the inevitable result is death, destruction and disaster.

CHAPTER ONE

Blizzard

"I was trying to make a little forward progress, but snow was flying in all directions at once and I couldn't even tell which way I was going. All I knew was that I had to somehow keep going. I had already given up any thought of getting to work. Looking back on it, I don't know what even made me try. I could see from my window that the streets were a raging mess of snow and ice, and hardly anything was moving. I guess it was habit that got me out into that storm. . . . There were . . . others like me. We'd bump . . . each other sometimes when a gust of wind would twirl me around.

"When I'd first started out, I tried to keep to the sidewalks, but they were so slippery that I fell twice in the first few steps, and then got down on my hands and knees and crawled. Out in the streets it wasn't quite so slippery, but I sure didn't have any idea which end was up.

"About the time I was giving up and starting back toward where I thought my apartment might be in that white, howling hell, I stumbled over something and fell flat on my face into a snowdrift that was over my head. For a while, I just wanted to lie there and give up, but something made me get up and start fighting again.

"Then I saw what it was I had tripped over. It was a pair of feet. They were sticking out of the drift in a pair of fur-lined rubber boots. I'll never forget those boots as long as I live. I don't know how long it took me to pull him out from under all that snow that had buried him, but when I got all through, it hadn't been any use. He was as stiff as a board, and his face was all mottled bluish and white where I could see flesh above his muffler. I don't know who he was. I tried to look around for a policeman, but there wasn't anybody in sight. I sure couldn't carry him anywhere. It was all I could do to stay on my own feet.

"Maybe it was wrong, but I just left him there. I knew he'd be found eventually, and there wasn't a thing I could do except get myself killed trying to do something about a dead body. . . . It took me about two hours to go back over the three blocks I'd travelled from my apartment.

"It was days before the chapping and swelling of the skin on my face went down. I guess I'll never get rid of the picture of that dead man's blue, frozen face. . . ."

This is how Harold Osterman described his own personal experience of one of the worst blizzards in modern history, the howling demon that struck the eastern seaboard as the winter season was ending in 1888. And the worst of it was, the blizzard seemed to blow up almost out of nowhere . . .

The New York Central Flyer left the depot at Buffalo, New York, on schedule at 5:00 P.M., Sunday, March 11, 1888. The weather that day had been pleasant in upstate New York, so warm that most of the passengers were convinced that spring was really on its way at last. None of them paid any attention as rain clouds gathered to the south, hovering ominously between the train and its destination. It was due in at Grand Central Station at 7:30 Monday morning.

Among the fifty-two Flyer passengers was a seventeen-year-old girl, Sara Wilson, on her way to visit an aunt who lived near Gramercy Park in New York. Sara would never reach the haven of her aunt's home. She was among the very first victims of a storm that would paralyze the eastern seaboard for days, claiming in its course over 200 lives and causing an estimated $20,000,000 in property damage.

The Blizzard of '88 remained vividly in the memories of all who lived through it and has now become almost a legend. It was an unprecedented holocaust of snow, hail, sleet and driving wind, depositing snow that later drifted into snowbanks three stories high in New York City. Its fury ravaged ten states, a dozen major cities, hundreds of towns and villages. One fourth of the nation's population experienced the freezing cold snow and wind of that one storm, and it has become the definitive measure of all similar storms.

Strangely, the blizzard arrived quite unexpectedly in the midst of sunny weather. In fact, the entire winter that preceded the blizzard was the mildest in seventeen years. The United States Signal Service weather observatory in New York City issued a forecast for Monday, March 12, which indicated fair weather, preceded by partial cloudiness near the coast, with Tuesday fair and warmer.

On Friday, March 9, Edward Meisinger had purchased at auction a carload of unclaimed snow shovels for his downtown department store. The shovels were delivered on Saturday, March 10, a warm and sunny day, amid jeers from Meisinger's fellow employees who promptly nicknamed him "Snow Shovel Ed," and referred to the snow shovels as "Edward's Folly."

On March 10, eight transatlantic steamers left New York Harbor along with a dozen sailboats. Six ocean liners were expected in the next two days, and dozens of freighters were heading for New York. The New York Pilot Fleet awaited them off Sandy Hook. William Inglis, a reporter for the New York *World*, was aboard Pilot Boat

No. 13, gathering information for a feature story on shipping in New York Harbor. It was a busy Saturday in the harbor, and the last thing on anyone's mind was impending catastrophe.

The Weather Bureau had its headquarters in the Equitable Building at 120 Broadway, where Sergeant Elias Dunn headed a four-man staff. Wind velocities were measured by an anemometer atop a tall pole. The headquarters was equipped with the latest meteorological equipment. Dunn was linked by telephone to Coast Guard Headquarters, the collecting station to which observers along the coast šent in hourly reports by carrier pigeon or telegraph. A telegraphic line also linked him to the central Weather Bureau in Washington, D.C. where information from across the country was received and interpreted.

When Dunn closed his Weather Bureau at midnight on Saturday, two major storm centers were moving eastward toward New York. The first had been spotted in Colorado on Friday; the second was moving north-northeast from Georgia. However, the Washington experts predicted that both disturbances would dissipate before reaching the eastern seaboard, and barely mentioned them in their ten o'clock transmission on Saturday night. On the basis of these inaccurate predictions Dunn wrote his forecast for Monday and closed up shop. The Weather Bureau would remain closed until 5:00 P.M., Sunday.

Early in the afternoon on Sunday, March 11, a cloudburst fell over New York, dissipating the

17

high spirits the warm weather had generated. By late afternoon, the rain had turned to sleet around Washington and Baltimore, and temperatures were diving. Ice on the overhead telegraph and telephone wires broke lines in a few places. By nightfall, with colder temperatures and no letup in the downpour, all the circuits to and from Washington were down.

In New York City, sidewalks, basements and cellars were flooded. The sewer system was unable to carry off the water. As temperatures fell with the oncoming night, the standing water turned to slick ice along roadways and sidewalks, disrupting the progress of the steam elevated railroads and slowing the horse-drawn streetcars.

The line of disturbance in the west spread from Lake Superior to the eastern edge of the Gulf of Mexico. The Georgia storm spread to the north and east, all the way to Cape Hatteras. On Sunday night the two low-pressure areas joined and formed a gigantic storm center off the New Jersey coast.

Even at this point the coming cataclysm might have blown out to sea, but another factor was added that proved decisive. A mass of freezing air from Canada moved in and held the giant storm center motionless, just on the edge of the commercial, industrial and population center of the country.

In 1888, transportation and communication were especially vulnerable. The rapid transit system of New York City moved on the surface. Long distance railroads carrying freight and passengers moved through deep cuts in the terrain which could be easily blocked by snowdrifts. Freight yards and terminals were in the open, unprotected.

Passenger traffic across the East River involved thousands of daily commuters between New Jersey, Brooklyn and Manhattan. The Brooklyn Bridge was the lone route across the river for surface traffic. If the ferries couldn't move across the river and the bridge was blocked, Manhattan Island would be effectively isolated.

The telegraph and telephone lines were all on the surface, miles of fragile wires strung out on poles. Electricity was carried through exposed cables. Gas pipes and water mains ran above ground.

Practically all the arteries which supplied the metropolis with power, water, food, medical supplies and all the other necessities to sustain life were exposed to the merciless elements.

By the time the Weather Bureau opened again at 5:00 P.M. on Sunday, a great deal of the damage had already been done and calamity was unavoidable. Neither the telephone nor the telegraph were working. The Coast Guard station at Peck's slip had no word from observers. Telegraph lines were down there, and no carrier pigeon could force its way through the growing gale.

On Sunday night, a luxury yacht, *Cythera*, went down with all hands. A huge French passenger steamer, *La Gascogne*, rolled hugely in the giant breakers, almost heeling over.

James Algeo, returning with his family to his

home in New York City on Sunday night from a visit in the Bronx, spent four hours traveling over the route that had taken him an hour to traverse earlier in the day. The horsecar and the elevated car had both been severely hampered by ice. It took the family nearly an hour to walk the two blocks from the elevated station to their home. The slick ice on the sidewalks and the wind-driven sleet and freezing temperatures reduced their progress to an inch at a time.

By midnight, the sleet had turned to snow.

At sea, weather conditions were terrifying. The sky was black with clouds. Hail, sleet and snow were driven by winds of hurricane force. Huge waves pounded the shore, crushing the steam tug *Thomas Crawford* against her pier. She went down with two men only a few feet from land. A steam ferry, *Hartford,* was smashed on the rocky shore of Long Island. The survivors huddled together in a deserted summer cottage, burning driftwood in the fireplace to keep from freezing.

Reactions to the storm varied a great deal depending on circumstances. At sea, the severity and danger of the situation were immediately apparent. On land, it was less apparent that an unprecedented situation was developing. The seriousness was obvious to weather observers and communications workers who were aware of the growing silence between isolated cities. But the majority of the people on the East Coast slept through the first hours of the storm.

Travelers on the railroad were among the

storm's earliest victims. In the early hours of the morning, the New York Central Flyer, with Sara Wilson and fifty-one other passengers, was more than five hours behind schedule. About two miles north of Albany, the engineer tried to ram the train through a monstrous drift. The engine car made it halfway through the drift and was almost buried in snow. The impact stopped the train so abruptly that the parlor car was derailed. A coal stove jerked and red-hot coals spilled out, setting fire to the car.

No one was hurt by the collision. A stranger dragged Sara Wilson from the smoking parlor car. The passengers stood in the storm, trying to decide what to do. The train would obviously not move, and several cars were now on fire. They decided to try and make it into Albany.

Floundering through the waist-deep drifts, Sara was quickly separated from the party, and slowly lost her strength. Succumbing to the cold, she fell backward into the snow and her body was covered in moments.

Along other tracks, another train struggled to make its 7:00 A.M. rendezvous with Grand Central Station. The Northern and Western Express was nearing Dobbs Ferry, hours behind schedule. Wind was keeping the tracks fairly clear and the train was moving at a good speed as the engineer tried to keep watch for flares through the all-obscuring wall of falling snow.

Ahead of the Northern and Western Express, the Chicago Express had been scheduled to pass Dobbs Ferry at 6:02 A.M. But at 6:37, the train had halted at a water tower south of the station. The conductor, Byron Calkins, set a flare on the tracks behind the train as it halted there. Once the boiler was filled, Calkins struggled against the wind and snow to remove the carbon flare. He was almost there when he heard a train whistle.

The Engineer of the Northern and Western saw the flare only minutes before impact. He grabbed the emergency air-brake cord and yelled to his fireman to jump. He pulled the brake cord again just seconds before the train hurtled into the baggage car of the Chicago Express. Ironically, in the middle of the worst snowstorm he had ever known, the engineer was boiled alive in a geyser of steam from the boiler of his train.

By the middle of the morning, thousands of passengers were stranded on snowbound trains throughout New England, Pennsylvania, New Jersey and Maryland.

Furniture in the cars was broken up and burned for warmth, but conditions on the stranded trains were close to unbearable. The water in washrooms froze and sanitation facilities were out of commission. Drinking water and box lunches were consumed quickly, and the passengers were left cold, hungry and thirsty in a frozen, white morass of boredom.

"Good Samaritans" brought coffee and sandwiches to some of the stranded trains and sold them at incredibly exorbitant prices, in one instance of the profiteering that continued in many ways throughout the days of the storm.

Restaurant owners in towns where travelers were stranded made fortunes overnight, charging $5.00 for a sandwich and $3.00 for a shot of whiskey.

Fifty inches of snow fell over Connecticut and eastern Massachusetts, drifts piled up to sixty feet in Hudson River Valley towns. The weight of fallen snow sank a train of coal barges being towed down the Hudson River. In Middletown, New York, drifts covered three-storied houses.

In New Haven, Connecticut, the bodies of three young girls were uncovered by shifting winds which blew away their snowy shroud on Monday afternoon. The town of Pittsfield, Massachusetts, was almost buried in twenty feet of snow.

In New York City, many people who arose on Monday morning looked out at the weather and grumbled about the snow, dressing warmly as they prepared to set out for work. They simply did not believe that already the city was, for all practical purposes, immobilized.

George D. Baremore spent grim moments struggling to the elevated station he normally used to commute to his downtown office. When he found a policeman, guarding the stairway, who announced that no trains were running downtown, he still was not convinced that the wisest course would be to return home. He set out to walk three blocks to another station. His frozen body was found deep in a snowdrift at Seventh Avenue and 54th Street hours later by two policemen.

The commuting hours between 7:00 A.M. and

9:00 A.M. saw a worsening of the storm on all fronts. The wind was so strong that waters were parted in Baltimore harbor and the Delaware River, revealing mud bottoms. In New York City, the winds had been averaging 36 miles an hour. During the morning the anemometer suddenly registered seventy-five miles an hour and then stopped working, frozen solid to its pole.

Sergeant Francis Long was part of the weather staff in the New York Weather Bureau that morning. Long had been the meteorologist of the Lady Franklin Bay Polar Expedition which had been trapped in the Arctic from 1881 to 1884. He had been one of seven men who had survived that icy ordeal out of the original party of twenty-five. He climbed to the top of the pole and chopped the ice away from around the wind meter, remarking later that conditions rivaled the worst the Arctic had produced.

Although the snowfall in New York City during March 12 and 13 was not record-breaking, the freezing temperatures, ranging between eleven degrees above zero and one below zero, and the howling, gale-force winds combined to create a grimly hazardous threat to life. Several hundred thousand New Yorkers attempted to reach their places of employment that Monday morning, despite the obvious difficulties, testifying to the fact that one of the primary human reactions to disaster is to refuse to recognize it.

Trees were uprooted and vans overturned by the winds. Drifts of snow driven by the winds piled up higher than second-story windows in several places of the grimly beleaguered city.

At Third Avenue and 76th Street, an elevated train stalled on the line. The steam train following it crashed into it, injuring fourteen men and women. The engineer of the second train, Samuel Towle, died of head injuries. After that accident, Colonel Frank Hain, General Manager of the Manhattan Railway Company, gave up his attempt to maintain service.

More than 15,000 people were marooned in elevated cars high above the streets. The weight of snow and people threatened collapse to the elevated structures. Wind might have toppled the cars. In another incident of profiteering, citizens propped ladders against the structures and sold passage to the streets at exorbitant prices.

James Algeo was one of only forty of the 1,200 employees of the American Bank Note Company who reached his job that morning. Despite the general lack of employees, some businesses flourished. Ed Meisinger made a profit of $1800 on his snow shovels. Shoe stores sold every pair of boots in stock.

At the stock market only 23 of the 600 members of the New York Stock Exchange showed up. The telegraphic ticker was silent. At the post office there was only a trickle of incoming mail. Those few school classes which managed to convene were dismissed almost immediately, and the children again struggled through the hazardous streets to make their way home. Four girls were found unconscious near City Hall Park and rescued by policemen.

Thousands of people, stranded in the city, crammed every kind of available shelter, including the bunks of the city's jails. Hotels profiteered, capitalizing on the situation to charge triple prices for rooms.

All the ferries had ceased operations by midday, and police finally closed the only remaining route off Manhattan Island—the Brooklyn Bridge— when the weight of fallen snow threatened to crush the fragile span.

James Algeo was dismissed early from his job. He searched for a place to spend the night and was unable to find one. It was a five-mile hike back to his home, and it took him more than five hours to make it. When he got to his own brownstone, he could hardly recognize it. A drift of snow nearly hid it.

Algeo's cheeks were cracked from the cold, his frostbitten nose was swollen, his coat was a glaze of solid ice. He ran in circles for a while outside his smothered house, calling his wife's name. He cried a little, and the tears froze to his cheeks. Finally he struggled up the drift and pounded frantically on the third-story windows. His wife eventually heard him and pulled him in. Algeo recovered, and was one of the very few in the city who survived three successive encounters with the fury of the storm.

Sam Randall, a Long Island farmer, was not so fortunate. He died in the snow only a few yards from the shelter of his home. In the country, cattle froze on their feet. In the city, thousands of sparrows froze in mid flight.

An ex-senator from New York, Roscoe Conkling, refused to pay a taxi driver fifty dollars to take him two and a half miles, and struggled through neck-high drifts to his New York Club. He collapsed on the doorstep, and died a month later of pneumonia.

On Staten Island, a seventeen-year-old boy, James Marshall, experienced a hair-raising episode which colored the rest of his life. He and two friends, Alexander Bennett and Charles Lee, normally commuted to their jobs at Elizabethport, New Jersey, Singer Sewing Machine Plant by rowing a mile across Staten Island Sound in a skiff. On Blizzard Monday, they made their way across the sound and hiked half a mile to the factory, only to find that it had been closed down. On their way back across the sound, wind and waves forced them off course. No sooner would a wave inundate them than the water froze on their clothing, encasing them in ice. After two hours, they finally made it to shore.

Bennett and Lee were barely conscious, Marshall in little better shape. He hauled his two friends out of the boat and dragged them to a haystack in a nearby field, covering them with hay to try and keep them warm. Marshall then began a race against death that he kept up for two days and nights. He trotted grimly around the haystack throughout that first agonizing night, knowing that if he stopped for a moment he would be gone. How he managed to keep moving until Wednesday will never be known.

A farmer looking for stray cattle came upon

him Wednesday morning, still staggering around the haystack. Bennett and Lee had both died on Monday night. Marshall was taken to a local doctor, who was forced to amputate his frozen hands and feet, but miraculously he survived.

Fires were a particular threat during the days of the storm, with telegraphic communications broken down, many fire trucks snowed in, and almost half the fire alarm boxes out of order.

In the early evening, fire broke out in a wooden factory building on Laight Street. The wind scattered sparks through the neighborhood, and only the still relentlessly falling snow kept it from turning a nearby row of tenements into a roaring conflagration. It was bad enough as it was. A full hour passed before the first fire-fighting equipment reached the area. It was another three hours before the blaze was under control. There were no casualties on Laight Street then, but at 2:00 A.M. Tuesday another fire broke out in a forty-family tenement, trapping several tenement dwellers in a tomb of flames.

The prices of food and basic commodities skyrocketed overnight as supply lines were cut off. It was almost impossible to obtain the coal vitally needed to heat buildings and ward off the still freezing temperatures.

The fall of snow finally abated early on Tuesday, and stopped in the late morning. But temperatures continued to hold around the zero mark. Wind slackened, but drifts continued to pile up

28

throughout the day. Slowly, cautiously, the people of ten states began to dig out.

In the aftermath of the blizzard, an additional hazard began to be revealed by the slowly melting snow. In the lower East Side streets, piles of garbage had begun to collect. The garbage collection system was broken down completely, and outbreaks of typhoid and smallpox were predicted by worried Health Commission officials.

The reporter William Inglis had survived the storm aboard Pilot Boat No. 13, but nine other pilot boats went down with all hands. For days, wreckage continued to wash ashore. From Sunday, March 11 through Tuesday, March 13, at least a hundred people had died at sea.

Even days after the snow had stopped falling, the blizzard continued to take its toll. On Tuesday afternoon, Richard Reilly, a young reporter on the New York *Star,* set out to confirm rumors that Coney Island had been engulfed by a tidal wave which had destroyed the famous Brighton Beach Hotel.

Reilly made it to Coney Island and found the Brighton Beach Hotel intact. His investigation caused him to miss the 3:00 P.M. train back to the city, but he decided to return that night with his story anyway. He hired a horse and sleigh at a livery stable and set out, confident that the weather could do him no harm. The temperature had risen to 35 degrees and it looked like the worst of it was over. But some time in the night Reilly ran out of luck. The exertion of his journey may have strained his heart and caused a heart attack. Foul play may have taken place, although an inquiry failed to unearth any evidence. Whatever the reason, Reilly fell from his sleigh into the snow. His body was found the next morning.

The storm passed out over the Atlantic and continued on its way, gathering force as it crossed the ocean. By Tuesday night, the British Isles were experiencing the worst snowstorm they had been through in a hundred years.

The complete communication breakdown that occurred as a result of the blizzard was apparently a lesson to the congressmen and senators in Washington who had been as isolated as everyone else. Within a few years, urban telegraph and telephone wires began to go underground and plans for subway systems were being developed. Never again would a sudden storm immobilize a population center so completely as had the Blizzard of '88. And never again would anyone assume that blizzards were something that swept through the wilds of the Dakota Territory, freezing a few cattle and moving on.

CHAPTER TWO

Tornado

"Each man almost involuntarily secured himself as best he might, and in an instant more the waterspout was upon us—with a roaring and bellowing as of a thousand demons, the cannonlike crash of breaking spars, the snapping of cordage, and the rending of timber. Then an irresistible rush of water poured down upon the deck, seemingly with the concussions of Niagara; it bore me back against the wheel casing and held me as in a vise, tore off my shirt and shoes and pressed with such a weight upon my chest that my eyeballs almost started from their sockets and I thought I had been caught under a falling spar.

"A moment of deathlike stillness succeeded this awful pandemonium and then the rain fell, not in drops but in solid masses that beat us down upon the deck, filled our eyes, mouths and nostrils, and nearly drowned us. The decks were afloat even with the tops of the demolished bulwarks; and ropes and half-alive but struggling men were washing back and forth as the ship's bare hulk rolled about in the trough of the sea.

"When I recovered from the shock of being half drowned and half crushed, and had succeeded in getting my breath and dashing the water from my eyes, I saw . . . the cabin was partly unroofed and the body of the captain's son was visible, jammed into a corner of the companionway, broken and crushed into an almost unrecognizable mass.

"As soon as they were able, the remnant of the crew crawled aft to the quarterdeck. Instead of our complement of twenty-five we only mustered eleven. The captain and mate were gone; the cook and steward had vanished with their galley. There were six of the men, one with a broken arm, the boatswain with a wound in his head deluging his face with blood, the carpenter, two of the boys, and myself left in command."

Thus does James J. Wait describe the effects of a waterspout in the Pacific in *Man Against Nature*. A waterspout is a tornadic wind formation which develops over water. A pendant or funnel-shaped cloud extends from the base of a cumulonimbus cloud to the surface of the water.

Worcester, Mass.: a 1953 tornado battered these apartment houses into kindling wood.

Tornado-force winds hit Waco, Texas, suddenly in 1954, leveling the downtown section.

This was a five-story department store before the cataclysmic Waco tornado struck it.

1954: Hurricane Carol drives the pounding surf into a tiny Connecticut coastal town.

1966: Hurricane Inez flattened Santo Domingo, leaving 200 victims in her bloody wake.

1889: a burst dam drowned Johnstown, Pa., in a sea
of rubble. Stores and houses collapsed; 2209 died.

1951: suddenly, without warning, an avalanche tore down a Swiss mountainside, burying this tiny town.

High winds scatter sparks and flames above Santa Barbara in this vicious 1964 blaze.

There its tip proceeds to wreak incalculable damage in the same manner as does its parallel wind formation on land—the tornado. In 1935, a tornado formed near Norfolk, Virginia, destroying trees and sheds. It crossed a creek, turning into a waterspout to lift small boats onto the shore and rip part of the pier apart. It changed back and forth between a waterspout and a tornado three more times, flinging railroad cars about as a tornado and sucking up creeks as a waterspout before it headed up Chesapeake Bay as a waterspout.

The most devastating of all windstorms is the dreaded tornado. The violent whirling inward and upward action of the winds is the main characteristic of both a tornado and a waterspout, and they are relatively identical phenomena. They occur in every part of the world, although tornadoes take place most frequently in the United States.

The conditions necessary for the occurrence of a tornado are not completely understood, and the mechanism of their formation is still somewhat obscure, although they are generally formed in conjunction with either strong cold fronts and squall lines or with thunderstorms, and are associated with instability in the lower layers of the atmosphere.

A tornado is probably the eeriest of all natural phenomena, with its menacing funnel shape clearly discernible on the horizon and its voracious tip that moves across the land in a caress of death.

In the northern hemisphere, the tornado season extends from March to October. Although tornadoes occur in all areas at every season, they are most frequent in April, May, and June at mid-continent. The states most frequently hit are Texas, Kansas and Oklahoma. Although the Great Plains are sometimes known as Tornado alley, and Texas is nicknamed the Cyclone State, a tornado did $700,000 damage in Washington, D.C. in 1927, and there is no area in which they have not been reported.

Tornadoes are most often single phenomena, but sometimes a dozen may form in the same day. They may last for a few seconds or up to several hours, have been recorded at widths from nine feet to two miles, and travel paths ranging from a few feet to nearly 400 miles.

Typical tornado weather is hot and sultry, and the sky is marked by strange colored clouds. The livid black and greenish-purple clouds that typically form tornadoes meet and crash together, setting up a whirling action which develops until the terrifying funnel begins to reach down to earth from its birthplace a mile high.

Once the tornado is fully formed it can move across the land at speeds of up to 65 miles per hour. Its violent action gives rise to a terrifying roar that can be heard miles away and an ominous whistling sound that changes to a noise like thunder as the tip of the funnel approaches.

Sometimes tornadoes are accompanied by thunderstorms with deluges of rain and hail. Sometimes lightning plays about the dark funnel, heightening the observer's impression that hell is on the loose. A faint smell of sulphur in the air might confirm a frightened observer's vision of the devil.

Tornadic forces are colossal almost beyond imagining. The electrical power of even a small tornado is in excess of the capacity of all the generating stations in the United States. The wind speed of the air composing a tornado defies measurement with present instruments, but anemometers have measured speeds up to 225 mph in other circumstances, so the tornadic winds surely exceed this figure.

Tornadic winds have driven small pieces of board into the ground to a depth of 18 inches, and subsequent tests revealed that those winds must have been travelling at the speed of a bullet shot from a revolver. Sand and gravel carried by the wind of a tornado can enter a human body like shotgun pellets.

The updraft within the whirling vortex of the tornado sucks objects from the ground as large as trees, automobiles and parts of houses. A tornado once ripped an iron bridge from its foundations and dropped it in a crumpled heap.

On June 22, 1919, a Minnesota tornado struck the Oriental Limited, throwing seven coaches from the rails. The baggage car was sucked up and set down thirty feet away.

On May 27, 1931, another Minnesota tornado lifted five 70-ton train coaches from the track and carried one of them 80 feet before laying it in a ditch.

There are numerous records of human beings

sucked into the vortex, carried in the air and dropped unhurt. An El Dorado, Kansas woman was sucked through a window and carried 60 feet in 1958, landing beside a broken phonograph recording of "Stormy Weather." A Higgins, Texas man was carried 200 feet over the treetops. At Lanark, Illinois in 1955, a car was lifted and carried 100 feet, then dropped right side up with its two occupants dazed but uninjured.

These seemingly apocryphal tales can be accepted by remembering that objects carried upward within the tornado frequently descend through an ascending air current which breaks the force of the inevitable fall.

In May 1953 a tornado smashed into Waco, Texas, and killed 114 people, injuring over 600 more, despite repeated warnings from the Weather Bureau. Many injuries and deaths resulted because people simply didn't believe the warnings. That same afternoon, another tornado killed eleven and injured sixty-six not far from Waco in San Angelo, Texas.

Two men were driving a car in Waco when the tornado struck. They were lifted two stories high in the air, still sitting upright in the car. The car settled gently to earth again with no damage, not even to the tires, but a dead woman's body was lying across the hood.

Ira J. Baden was in Waco, Texas, on its dark Monday and his eyewitness account of his experiences is horrifying. Baden clung desperately to a steel rail in the heart of the business district

36

of Waco during the forty-five seconds that the tip of the tornado devastated almost everything in his view.

He saw buildings exploding outward, and automobiles crushed like insects by falling debris. One car leapt upward into the air and disappeared.

The people of Waco had paid little attention to the Weather Bureau warnings. There was a widely accepted legend of immunity to tornadoes in Waco, a sort of general agreement that "it can't happen here" that caused most of the population to ignore the possibility of cataclysm in much the same way that New Yorkers refused to believe the evidence of their own eyes on Blizzard Monday, 1888.

In Waco, as in most other areas, rescue work began almost immediately. Baden reports that his ears were still popping as the air pressure returned to normal in the wake of the tornado and a clerk in a nearby store began cleaning watches and jewelry out of the window to discourage possible looters. In the drenching downpour everyone who had survived the ravages of those forty-five seconds of destruction began to search for other survivors.

Even the most levelheaded of the survivors were dazed and some were in shock. One man took off his jacket to begin digging in the rubble and handed it to a girl who folded it neatly and put it in a drugstore refrigerator.

By the time private citizens had dug into the tons of debris that buried the collapsed roof of a cafe, firemen had arrived and organized a kind of bucket brigade to aid in the removal of rubble. A badly injured woman and a scratched and bruised man were dug out still alive, but the arms and legs of other victims sticking out of the huge pile of junk showed no signs of life.

Searching for any indication of a still living survivor, Baden heard voices calling for help from inside a movie theater. The naked feet of a man stuck out of one pile of rubble, but Baden could find no pulse in either one of the oddly twisted ankles. He was joined by several others who eventually found a way into the theater and dug away rubble until they were able to free two men still alive.

Near the passageway, Baden could hear the voice of Miss Lillie Matkin calling for help from beneath tons of debris, the remains of the collapsed Dennis Furniture Company where she had been operating the telephone switchboard. Rescue workers immediately began digging down toward her voice. Miss Matkin clung to life throughout that long, terrifying night, and was hoisted from what might have been her grave at 6:45 the next morning. Rescuers had worked in continuous shifts throughout her fourteen-hour ordeal.

The tornado had struck the business district of Waco shortly after 4:30 in the afternoon, and by 5:00 nearly 10,000 people had gathered around the area. Most of them were not heroic rescue workers, however. Or even looters, the parasites who capitalize on the worst disasters. They were merely onlookers—sightseers, sharing what seems to be a universal human impulse to have a look at disaster.

The variety of motives that make up this impulse to gather at the scene of a disaster cover a range that perhaps begins with a desire for a vicarious taste of violence at a glimpse of a crushed body or severed limb and extends into an enthusiastic self-congratulations on having missed the consequences of disaster oneself.

In the huge crowds that gathered around downtown Waco on the afternoon of the tornado were many people awaiting news of friends and loved ones who had been in the disaster area when the tornado hit. The experiences of those survivors who have been touched by the catastrophic event through their loved ones are an intrinsic part of the network of emotional trauma that follows in the wake of most disasters.

At Waco those survivors who were intimately connected to the event through their loved ones were forced to go through an agony of anxiety that might, in the end, have been easier in its way than the kind of certainty presented by two bodies found inside a car. The car had been crushed by so much brick and mortar that it was flattened to the level of the wheels. The two bodies had to be cut out of the wreckage with a torch.

In Waco, rescue forces were swiftly mobilized. By 5:30 P.M. rescue crews of Army and Air Force men attacked the debris, uncovering such grisly horrors as the two bodies flattened into bloody pancakes in the wreckage of the automobile, while MP's and National Guardsmen kept a semblance of order among the onlookers and waiting relatives, preventing much of the looting and profiteering that springs up at the scene of a disaster when the control of such authorities is absent.

In contrast to the exaggeratedly self-interested behavior of individuals who loot through wreckage and hang endlessly on at the scene, hampering rescue work, there is also the useful and necessary impulse which, in this case, led thousands of people across the country to send bandages, blankets, food, money and blood to the aid of the stricken town.

The two impulses seem to exist side by side and are manifested in varying proportions in every disaster. There is always a substantial segment of the population which is ready to contribute time, money, and goods and services to aid a community suddenly stricken by catastrophe. It is this impulse, by and large, which makes it possible for stricken communities to recover.

Without the hours of rescue work, relief work and help of all kind that were generously donated to help the people of Waco begin to put themselves back together, there is a great danger to the survival of the community after such a disaster.

In 1955, the township of Udal, Kansas, was literally destroyed by a tornado. The tiny community of 610 people inhabited 187 dwellings, 170 of which were smashed to rubble by the twister that blew Udal off the map on the night of May 25. Sixteen more houses were damaged beyond repair, and only one escaped with no damage.

Eighty people were killed outright, and 270 more were injured. One of the men who survived without serious injuries was actually ripped out of his shoes and thrown into a tree. Another group of lucky ones was the Norman Lanning family, huddled against their kitchen wall. When the tornado moved on, that wall was the only thing left standing in the entire area, and it saved their lives.

For the township of Udal, there was no possibility of community survival after that night of destruction.

For Waco, survival was possible, but the process of rebuilding was a grim and terrible business as people recounted their experiences. One man had been trying to reach the building where his wife was working when he was snatched up by the wind and simply disappeared.

Another man was sitting at his desk in his second-floor office when the tornado struck. The wind tore off the roof and front and side walls of his building. The man walked to the edge of the open floor and looked dazedly over the edge. Then he retreated to the remaining wall and opened the door, expecting to retreat further into a hallway. The door opened onto empty space. Unbelieving, the man stepped into space.

In the streets, automobiles were whirled sideways along the streets, many of them occupied. Some only stopped their careening progress when they were squashed by falling debris. People inside were either crushed to death or entombed by the piles of rubble and died shortly.

All over the city, buildings which had remained apparently intact had to be evacuated because of escaping gas from damaged gas mains. Many people huddled hopelessly together, barely reacting when warning of a possible second tornado was issued. They weren't capable of absorbing any more shock.

On several occasions, tornadoes have struck in the same place twice. On May 4, 1922, Austin, Texas was hit twice in half an hour, as was Baldwyn, Mississippi on March 16, 1942. In Ellis County, Oklahoma, a tornado destroyed almost every structure in the entire area on April 9, 1947. When a second tornado hit the same area on May 31, there was virtually nothing left to damage.

The emotional stress of disaster takes a physical as well as a psychological toll. Nausea, dizziness, jaundice, dermatitis, falling hair, vomiting, high temperature, and sleeplessness are all predictable in high frequencies in a community during the weeks that follow a disaster.

People's eating habits change. Their daily lives are conducted in new and different ways. Sometimes it takes months for the mental images associated with the disaster to fade from conscious memory, and even longer for them to cease to crop up in nightmares. For most people who undergo the kind of ordeal a natural disaster such as a tornado presents, life never again seems quite the same.

A month after the Waco disaster, the town of Worcester, Massachusetts, lay sweltering in the heat of a Tuesday afternoon in midsummer. It was typical tornado weather that day, June 9, 1953. People were tense and irritable with the oppressive, sticky heat. In midafternoon, the sky began to look strange, with peculiar cloud formations that looked like black castles in the air. The clouds continued to mount until they passed out of range of the radar tracking station at the weather laboratory at the Massachusetts Institute of Technology. People expected a thunderstorm, but very few were aware that earlier in the afternoon a U.S. Air Force weather plane had spotted a small tornado in the area.

At 4:30 in the afternoon, Mr. and Mrs. George Jones watched the birth of a tornado that would come screeching down on Worcester and several surrounding towns before the day was over. Jones said that as the clouds began to spin, he heard a roar that sounded like 10,000 jet airplanes flying overhead. The funnel first slashed at the ground in a pleasant meadow near the Jones farm twenty-five miles northwest of Worcester. It sucked a six-foot crater 100 feet in diameter out of the meadow and took off across the fields, snatching up trees, a barn and a house. In another few minutes the tornado's tip was a half mile wide, and it was traveling fast, spewing rain, thunder, lightning and hailstones, some of which were over ten inches across.

Six miles away, the town of Barre lay directly in its path. Forty Barre homes were ripped to shreds and two men were left dead before the furious whirlwind passed on.

The tornado hit Rutland, a town of 3,056 inhabitants, at a speed of forty-nine miles per hour. Donald Marsh, principal of the Rutland grammar school, was killed when his car capsized. His six-year-old daughter had a tree branch impaled in her chest.

In Holden, another small suburb, one hundred and seventy houses were hopelessly damaged, and 160 others suffered severe damage. The tornado left eight people dead and 200 injured before it was through with Holden. Tiny Charles Oslund, only fifteen days old, was ripped out of his mother's arms and disappeared in the wind. His body was found three days later. By the time the tornado hit Worcester, its winds were rotating at a speed of 500 mph with a force ten times that of the atomic bomb that mutilated Hiroshima.

Worcester had a population of 200,000 in 1953. It was primarily a factory town, and most of its men were on their way home from work at eight minutes past five that afternoon. The thunderstorm had already begun, dumping torrents of rain on the hapless city, and not many saw the tornado smashing in from the northeast.

A woman and a small boy were struggling against the wind outside a lumberyard when a huge trailer truck descended on them from the sky, crushing them instantly to death. Near there 150 priests and nuns huddled praying while the tornado ripped off the fourth story of Assumption College. Blocks of houses in suburban sections of the city were all blasted to splinters.

Bill Porter was asleep in a second-floor apartment in a million-dollar low-income housing project in Great Brook Valley. His mother shook him awake and he grabbed his baby. The three never made it to the stairs. The house was rocking like a small boat, and Porter heard a horrible whistling, groaning sound as the tornado hit.

William Kensington saw his car rise into the air, travel a hundred feet and drop into a pile of junk.

A man lugging a crate of eggs saw the eggs pop out of the crate, but they didn't fall to the ground. This was the result of the vacuum effect inside the tornado caused by differences in air pressure inside and out. This same vacuum effect whirled other children out of their mothers' arms, and frantic women reached after some of those children and hauled them out of the air like kites.

A city bus was caught in the furious grip of the tornado and somersaulted forty feet, crushing a pedestrian to death and smashing through the brick wall of an apartment house. As the driver was helping to free his injured and dead passengers, the almost severed end of his thumb kept dangling annoyingly in their faces. He kept trying to bite it off.

There were other grotesque injuries. A teenage girl was dropped three floors to the street with both her legs blown off. A seven-year-old girl had her legs sheared off by a flying refrigerator. A small boy was shielding his sister with his body when he was stabbed in a dozen places by broken glass.

At the Home Farm, a city institution for the aged and the poor, the tornado left seven dead.

At eighteen minutes after five, the tornado screamed out of Worcester heading for Shrewsbury, a town five miles to the east. In Shrewsbury, Mrs. Norma Fuller was decapitated by a tree limb. Her seventy-two-year-old neighbor, Arthur Wilson, was blown a quarter of a mile away from his house.

At Shrewsbury, the tornado split. One part headed southeast. The other headed east, killing five and injuring sixty-two in nearby Westboro. Two more died in Southboro, and more in Fayville, before the tornado was spent.

In its wake were ninety-two dead. The 1,310 injuries included fractured skulls, broken hips and ribs, and broken and severed limbs. Eyes had been chewed up by flying gravel. Internal organs were injured. Hundreds of people had pieces of flesh gouged out by glass.

Sixty million dollars' worth of property damage left ten thousand people homeless. Fires raged uncontrollably in the injured towns. There were blocks and blocks of total devastation.

As rescue workers attempted to help pick up the pieces, horrible injuries were revealed. A woman had a wound in her thigh where a two-by-four had been driven completely through it. Hundreds of others were bleeding and dazed.

The shock of those savage ten minutes had been tremendous. Many people were completely disoriented. One woman began to wash the wall of her kitchen, despite the fact that the other three walls were completely gone. A man began to trim the lawn in front of his house, seemingly unaware that the house itself was gone and behind him there was only a gaping hole.

Police and firemen worked heroically to quell the fires despite not knowing if their own families were safe. The hospitals were in chaos. The morgues had only a fraction of the capacity needed to handle the dead bodies.

There are an average of 150 tornadoes every year, causing almost twice that many deaths. A batch of sixty tore through Mississippi, Alabama, the Carolinas, Tennessee, Kentucky and Indiana in 1884 killing 424 people in one day. Eight tornadoes killed 792 people in Missouri, Illinois, Indiana, Kentucky, Tennessee and Alabama on March 18, 1925. Only the night before the ordeal in Worcester, a tornado had killed 116 in Beecher, Michigan.

A man overtaken by the Beecher tornado was picked up by the wind as he reached the steps of his house. He was thrown into a tree, and then pulled along the grass. He ended up against the basement wall of his house on his head. As he lay there, still conscious, he saw his house rising on its foundations. The wind grabbed him and took him back up into the air. He landed again in his basement, and part of the front porch fell in on his legs.

In the period from 1916 to 1961, the U.S. Weather Bureau reports that 11,056 tornadoes occurred in the United States, killing 9,397 people and injuring about 13 people for every one killed.

Advance warning of tornadoes can save lives if people heed the warnings and take shelter. It is possible to detect the presence of a tornado from many miles away due to the fact that electrical discharges from a tornado cloud send out radio waves of unusually high frequency which can be easily identified as an indication of the presence of a tornadic cloud formation even before the tornado is formed. Radar can be used fairly efficiently for tracking tornadoes already formed. Thus warning systems can work fairly accurately and provide some safeguard against loss of life, provided people follow the warnings and take precautions, such as taking shelter.

However, at this time the prevention of tornadoes is impossible. The total masses of air involved are so vast that it would take a massive nuclear explosion to influence them, and obviously the consequences in that case would be as damaging as the tornado. At the present time, tornadoes cause a formidable amount of damage and destroy considerable human and physical resources each year, and remain a sudden and terrifying threat and one of nature's most awesome manifestations of disaster.

CHAPTER THREE

Hurricane

"I had gone to sleep the night before with no feeling that I was in any danger. We knew a hurricane was moving north towards us, but we thought she was going to blow out to sea before she got here. When I woke up that morning, wind was shrilling around the cottage like a hundred banshees, and the whole cottage was shaking. Before I was even awake, I knew something horrible was happening.

"I got over to the window and looked out, but the rain was pounding against the window and I couldn't see anything. Once it cleared for a second and I could see sea water pouring over the dunes in front of the cottage. Pieces of flying wood were slamming against the house and it sounded like I was being bombed.

"By the time part of the roof came off and one of the cottage walls came crashing down into the living room, I wasn't even thinking. I just crouched in a heap in the hallway, staring out at the end of the world.

"I saw two people staggering toward me through the blinding rain. Their bodies were covered with blood where sand was hitting them with hundreds of tiny nicks. All of a sudden a board came flying toward them and decapitated one of them. It was horrible. First there was the two of them, then I saw the board, and then one of them just didn't have a head.

"The other one dropped down and kept on crawling toward me. He came in right over the pile of junk that had been the living room and slumped down a few feet away from me up against the wall of the hallway. After a while the water started rising and I somehow managed to pull him with me up the stairs to the second floor. We just stayed there together. I watched things whirling by sometimes where a big part of the roof was gone, but mostly I kept my eyes shut. I don't know if I'll ever get that shrieking sound of the wind out of my ears. . . ."

This was the experience of Mrs. Audrey Burkett during the morning of August 31, 1954, as Hurricane Carol slammed against the New England coastal town of Oak Bluffs. After the flooding waters receded, Mrs. Burkett and her stranded companion searched for the body of his wife. He and his wife had been trying to make for higher ground when tons of water made it impossible to progress further in their automobile. They had left it and run toward Mrs. Burkett's cottage seeking shelter. The abandoned automobile was never found. But the body of the man's wife was found, bloated and covered with flies, lying across a sand dune. They weren't able to find the head.

Hurricane Carol began as a small low pressure area east of the Leeward Islands. Weather observers noted the low pressure, assuming it had dritfed across the Atlantic from the west coast of Africa. It might have developed anywhere, since the pressure drop at its center was so slight no ship had reported it.

Far to the north, the Bermuda high, a huge permanent high-pressure area, straddled the western Atlantic. Moving eastward across the United States was another large mass of high pressure. It came from Siberia.

On August 25, 1954, a meteorologist marked the spot just east of the Bahamas where the low pressure area had begun to intensify. On August 26, the low pressure area had moved north to the top of the Bahamas and had grown sufficiently intense to be called a storm center. At that point it acquired a name—Carol.

It was moving along at a leisurely pace, gathering in intensity as the surrounding air moved into its low pressure center with increasing velocity. On the twenty-ninth, it changed course and began moving in a northwesterly direction, darkening skies along the Carolina coast. Weather reporters began to alert the southern coast.

Carol was still moving slowly forward, but winds circulating about the eye of the storm were increasing to hurricane velocity. On the thirtieth, a U.S. tanker reported winds over a hundred miles per hour and thirty-foot waves in the hurricane. Carol had become a force to be reckoned with.

On the thirtieth, she changed her course again and began moving steadily north. The Carolina coast suffered some damage, but was spared the major violence of a direct hit by that course change. Carol was now a vast whirlpool of hurricane winds covering a circular area 160 miles in diameter, with trails of storm-force winds covering an even larger area. But for a while, her forward progress was blocked. The Siberian high and the Bermuda high had met and forced the progress of the hurricane to a standstill.

Then, with the leisurely indifference of all natural forces, the two high pressure areas drifted apart. The trough of lower pressure which opened up between them was like a path at Carol's feet, and it led northward directly over the New England States. Carol didn't hesitate. Within moments she began moving north, picking up speed —from 2 or 3 miles an hour to 40 miles an hour.

In twenty-four hours she was over Long Island. During the night she had stayed nearly a hundred miles offshore in her northward progress, but her trailing winds had nevertheless flicked violence along the coast, smashing boardwalks, piers and jetties all the way. Small boats were wrenched from their moorings and flung against breakwaters and pilings like so many wood chips. People in Virginia, Maryland, Delaware, Pennsylvania, and New Jersey saw the evidence of Carol's seaward passage in the wreckage of their coast.

At 9:00 A.M. on the morning of August 31, Carol struck Long Island. Trees, power lines and TV antennas fell before her 125-mile-per-hour winds. A road to the eastern end of the island crumbled beneath water rushing in from the sea, and 4,500 people were stranded at land's end. Surging flood tides and raging surf were piling up on the Connecticut-Rhode Island shore as Carol headed for New England.

By 10:30 A.M. Carol smashed into the shore of Connecticut. Salt spray and sand withered the leaves of trees left standing, and for days plants far inland curled and died. Electric power was cut off as poles and lines fell. Telephones failed. Immense storm waves simply swallowed up people and cars. One thirty-five-foot wave swept up a Rhode Island beach and wiped out 300 houses with a single swipe.

Carol moved relentlessly across Massachusetts, flattening crops, toppling church steeples and felling huge elms, maples and oaks along village streets. But on land, the hurricane began to encounter hills and mountains which blocked her streaming currents or deflected them from their spiral path. The velocities of her winds began to drop. By the time she reached the Canadian border, she was dead.

Behind her, she had left a swath of terrible destruction. Sixty people had died, a thousand people were injured. Economic losses were staggering. The total destruction from North Carolina to Maine amounted to more than $461,000,000.

Even as exhausted New Englanders struggled to regain a semblance of normalcy, another hurricane, Dolly, was heading northward from the Bahamas. Dolly curved eastward before she hit New England.

A week later, on September 6, another low pressure area in the Atlantic began to grow. By the seventh, it had developed hurricane-force winds and acquired a name—Edna. Edna flooded low-lying areas, but moved past the Carolinas without more serious damage.

The Weather Bureau could not accurately predict Edna's course, and once again the people of New England waited, still trembling from the task of cleaning up after Carol. Edna passed quickly over Maine and died over New Brunswick by the night of the eleventh, but before she died, she killed twenty-one more people in New England.

By the end of September, Carol and Edna had passed into legend and people were tired of talking about the weather. Life was beginning to resume its normal course, and people were beginning to look forward to Halloween.

Then on October 5, weathermen spotted another low pressure area a thousand miles south of the Carolina coast. A reconaissance plane found Hazel in the Windward Islands. Her winds had already reached 95 miles per hour. She was relatively small, but intense. That night, she knocked down a few houses and uprooted a few palm trees on the islands of Grenada and Carriacou, but they were the aimless swipes of a baby.

By October 12, Hazel had grown up. Trailing violent, flailing arms of wind and cloud, Hazel was slowly growing and gathering force. Her path was erratic. She hesitated near the Dutch West Indies, moved toward Nicaragua, and then suddenly turned north. During the tenth of October she continued turning east and north until she was pointed toward the Republic of Haiti. She had made up her mind.

On the western end of the island, she so totally devastated life that for the survivors, even the means of sustaining life were gone. Thousands of primitive fishermen were left homeless, without food, and without the means of getting food. Fishing boats were smashed to unidentifiable wreckage on the beach. Countless Haitians left alive after her passage died as a result of her devastation.

Passing over the Bahamas, Hazel now headed for the Carolina coast. Twice before during the season, Carol and Edna had bypassed the Carolinas, but now a third storm, the most intense of the year, was moving into position, and this time the Carolinas would not escape.

On the morning of October 15, Hazel hit at the coast with her maddened arms. Twenty-foot waves hurtled to shore on a ten-foot tide and the low lands were obliterated in a seething cascade of water. Winds of up to 150 miles per hour reduced structures to matchsticks. At Ocean Drive Beach, a three-story hotel blew into the sea. At Crescent Beach, 527 houses were flattened. At Garden City, a concrete block store crumpled, and the second story went sailing into the air and landed 150 yards from the pulverized foundation.

An eyewitness to the damage along the coast reported:

"All traces of civilization on that portion of the immediate water front between the state line and Cape Fear were practically annihilated. . . . The greater part of the material from which the houses had been built was washed from one to two hundred yards back into the edge of low-lying woods which cover the leeward side of the islands. . . . The greater portion of this material is ground to unrecognizable splinters and bits of masonry. . . . In most cases it is impossible to tell where buildings stood. Where grassy dunes stood there is now only flat white sandy beach."

Hazel moved north and inland from the Carolinas, refusing to be intimidated by the irregularities of the land. Continuing north, Hazel hurtled the Alleghenies and headed toward Toronto. An approaching cold front from Alaska was also heading toward Toronto. The rainfall that resulted when Hazel's great mass of moist warm air met that cold air from the north resulted in a disaster on a scale Toronto had never before experienced.

Within six hours more than three hundred million tons of water came from Hazel's clouds onto the steeply sloping land behind Toronto. Hours after the fury of the storm center had passed over the town, the millions of tons of water began to raise rivers and streams. With an earth-shaking roar, the cataracts swept down on Toronto, burying whole communities under water. Houses were swept from their foundations. Men, women and children were swept to an icy, watery death. Thirty-five bridges collapsed in the torrent, plunging cars laden with doomed lives into the dark, roaring water.

The water continued to rise. People clung to the roofs of their houses, and then let go and were washed away by the waters of death. Men trying to rescue neighbors perished with them.

Finally, Hazel began to dissipate her strength. She got as far as Greenland, and her winds were felt as far away as the coast of Norway. Seventy-eight people had died in Canada, ninety-five in the United States, six in the Bahamas. In Haiti, loss of life among the natives was estimated at close to a thousand. Across the path of her furious charge were scattered the bodies of her victims, amid the devastated wreckage of what had once been a series of thriving communities.

A hurricane is essentially a rotating cyclone of the tropic oceans. When well developed it is a vast whirlwind of extraordinary violence. It is neither the largest nor the most intense of all storms. Temperate Zone storms are usually larger than the hurricane, and it cannot match the concentrated fury of the tornado. But because of its considerable size and great intensity, it is the most dangerous and destructive of all storms. In total damage, hurricanes have exceeded any other natural catastrophe.

The term "hurricane" is defined technically as a storm of tropical origin with a cyclonic wind circulation of 74 mph or higher. The term "hurricane winds" is used to denote any wind of 74 mph or higher and is not confined to the winds of a real hurricane.

The Pacific counterpart of the Atlantic hurricane is the typhoon. The term "cyclone" is used technically to describe any rotating storm. Hurricanes are tropical cyclones. A cyclone is any system of rotating winds, except a tornado, which exists in a class by itself.

The destructive effects of hurricanes are usually the result of a combination of several forces, including the high velocity winds, solid objects carried by those winds, water from increased levels of the sea, huge tides and waves and torrential rainfall. Buildings and people both are subjected to all of these destructive forces in various combinations when a hurricane hits.

Much of the damage to buildings is accomplished by pressure exerted by the wind. The pressure exerted on a surface increases geometrically with the wind velocity. When the wind velocity is 50 miles per hour, the force is about 10 pounds on an area of one square foot. At 100 miles per hour, it is about 40 pounds per square foot. Winds of up to 150 mph have been recorded in hurricanes, with gusts of even higher velocities. A wind of average hurricane velocity pushing against a wall 40x12 feet, exerts a force of about 24 tons on that wall. Little wonder that buildings collapse like so many card houses.

A street devastated by a hurricane so closely resembles a bombed-out area that it is sometimes difficult to detect differences between the effects of a hurricane and the effects of that most devastating of all man-made catastrophes—war. In primitive areas, houses are utterly demolished along with trees and other vegetation. Uprooted trees may be stripped of leaves, limbs and even bark. A hurricane can turn a flourishing orchard into a wasteland of whitened, dying stumps.

The destruction brought about by sheer force of wind alone is vividly depicted in the following account of the damage done to the harbor at St. Thomas on October 29, 1867, observed by Louis V. Housel and recorded in *Man Against Nature:*

"The first view of the scene impressed us with the terrible power that had been running riot among the shipping. The harbor was literally choked with wrecks; and, as if not content with that, some of the smaller craft were flung high upon the rocks. Vessels of all sizes became unmanageable, and were driven hither and thither about the harbor by the violence of the merciless gale, driving upon and sinking each other.

"One large collier, in ballast, the *British Empire* by name, broke from her moorings and charged three times across the harbor, maneuvered by the shifting wind, sinking steamers, ships and schooners, until, shattered and stove, she finally sank upon the wrecks of two Danish brigs she had sent to the bottom before her."

The hurricane wrecked more than sixty vessels of all sizes, from an iron steamer to a small coasting schooner, and drowned over six hundred persons. It was one of the really great hurricanes of the century, known in Puerto Rico as "San Narciso," after the old custom of naming hurricanes after the Saints on whose days they occurred. In many parts of the island, it is considered the most violent hurricane ever experienced in that part of the world. The center passed over the town of Caguas, with a calm lasting ten to twelve minutes. The storm was relatively small in diameter, moving rapidly and with terrific violence.

In addition to the hazard presented by the force of the wind itself, objects carried by these high-velocity winds become a kind of heavy artillery, bombarding anything above ground with unbelievable force. In the Puerto Rican hurricane of 1928, a one-inch-thick plank was driven through a sixteen-inch palm tree by the wind. A similar phenomenon was reported on July 26, 1825, during a hurricane at Guadeloupe. Heavy tiles and shingles from houses which are being dimantled by the wind also become fearful projectiles, hurtled with deadly force by hurricane winds.

Many of the wounds and deaths which occur during hurricanes are the result of these projectiles, which can fearfully maim or kill in the space of an instant.

When the sea rises and joins forces with the wind, the resulting destruction is usually complete. Buildings not already lifted off their foundations by the winds are undermined by the water and toppled by wave motion, to complete their demolition. Buildings moved by wind and water act as battering rams against other structures. Whole sections of cities become a vast mass of floating wreckage, carried on by a rising sea, sweeping everything before it.

Ships, torn from their anchorages, are carried by the swelling water and sometimes left high and dry miles inland when the sea recedes. Other ships are driven against piers, bridges and wharves, where they batter those structures to pieces.

Amidst the floating debris are many heavy objects such as telegraph and telephone poles, beams and tree trunks. The combined onslaught of such a mass thrown with terrific force by monstrous waves and winds, combines to batter down any remaining structures. Huge rocks are washed loose and pitched on the shore like so many cannon balls. Few structures can withstand the onslaught that the combination of all these factors presents. Frail human beings, caught in the wreckage and assaulted by gigantic forces, stand little chance of survival.

Usually, the electric, telephone and telegraph lines are thrown down. Communication fails. As night falls, the inhabitants of the stricken area are left in darkness. Sometimes the water supply fails as wells, cisterns, and pipe lines are broken and contaminated by the overflow of the sea. Sanitary conditions become deplorable. Crops have sometimes been wiped out and stores of food destroyed by the wind. Thousands of survivors are left shelterless. Disease often follows in the wake of the destruction.

In addition, moisture picked up by storms over the ocean begins to saturate the clouds. When it condenses, torrential rains inundate the area of the storm. In some cases, as in Toronto in 1954, floods caused by runoff bring about far more destruction and death than caused by the original hurricane's passage.

The downpour in a hurricane is so intense that sometimes people who might otherwise have survived are dazed by it and wander into their own destruction. Water rises so rapidly that in low-lying areas, many people are caught in cars and are underwater before they realize what is taking place, unable to escape, trapped in an underwater tomb, drowning horribly in what was supposed to be a means of escape.

Waves and surges from the sea, especially if they are combined with a rising tide when the hurricane hits, can sometimes cause more damage than any other aspect of the storm.

In Galveston, Texas, during one of the worst

hurricanes of all time in 1900, the water rose constantly for four and a half hours while the storm raged. Suddenly the water level rose four feet in a few seconds as the storm wave struck. In those few seconds the rising water took a grim toll. Six thousand people were drowned.

The hurricane season of 1957 saw five tropical storms blow up out of the Gulf of Mexico and hit the coastline of the United States. Of the five, the most important was Audrey, one of the great hurricanes of the century. Audrey was a killer.

She was first detected on the 25th of June just north of the Bay of Campeche in the lower Gulf. For two days she moved almost due north, heading straight for the coast of Louisiana.

A Navy Hurricane Hunter plane penetrated the eye of the storm and found winds of 104 miles per hour. The highest official report was 105 mph at Sulphur, Louisiana, before the anemometer blew away. An oil rig unofficially reported winds of 180 mph at the height of the storm.

The New Orleans Weather Bureau began issuing warnings on the first day. By 10:00 A.M. on the 26th, the watch warnings were changed to hurricane warnings. Hurricane winds would begin along the Louisiana coast on Wednesday night, June 26th, bringing tides that would range from five to eight feet above normal along the coast by Thursday. By 10:00 P.M. Wednesday night, the advisory warned that tides might reach nine feet.

In the town of Cameron, citizens heard the warnings. Much later controversy would develop around those warnings, after more than six hundred dead bodies were found in the wake of Audrey's furious progress.

Before the arrival of Audrey, Cameron was a quiet town. Its older residents had been in the area for generation after generation, some of them tracing their family trees back to the days of the early French settlers of the area. There was also a sizeable group of "newcomers," families who had settled in the area shortly after World War II.

There was no noticeable friction between the two factions, but Audrey would draw a line between them. The old-timers chuckled when the newcomers listened with terror to the hurricane warnings, and smiled to each other as the newcomers gathered a few possessions and chucked the children into the car, leaving for higher ground to the north. After Audrey was gone, it was mostly the newcomers who had survived. The old-timers, staunch in their disregard of Weather Bureau warnings, had paid little attention to the cloudy sky. And hours later, in hundreds, they died.

The water began to rise on Thursday morning at the rate of 1.5 feet per hour until it reached a record high of 11.7 feet. Waves of great height rolling in from the Gulf, pushed by winds of up to 150 mph, raised that high to much more in surges. Frame houses, built only a few feet above sea level and sheltered by sand dunes and ridges with elevations of only five and six feet, were swept away by the dozen and shoved along on the storm tide.

In the whirling mass of the tide, the structures bumped against each other and butted up against concrete structures, many of them splintering into smaller and smaller pieces of wreckage as the buffeting continued.

The village of Creole, twelve miles east of Cameron, was completely destroyed. Only one building remained standing when the storm passed. People clung to rooftops, floating timbers, and anything else that promised to keep their heads out of water. One by one, whitened fingers let loose their frantic hold. One by one, people slipped quietly off precarious perches into the raging maelstrom of the flood.

In a tiny community east of Creole, Oliver Boudreau and his wife escaped death by climbing onto the roof of their barn. They hung on for thirty hours as the roof became a portion of a roof and finally only slatted remnants.

Horses, cows and other livestock were drowned by the hundreds. On Friday morning, the sand dunes were strewn with the bloated bodies of animals and humans in gruesome juxtaposition. All living things had been helpless before the onslaught of Audrey's fury.

The fetid smell of death and decay hung over

the land for days. And here and there in the wreckage bobbed grotesquely a concrete vault from one of Cameron's cemeteries, where flood waters had disinterred the concreted remains of dozens who had died long before Audrey came on the scene. There was no sanctuary from Audrey —not even in the grave.

In the aftermath of the storm, the Weather Bureau was made the primary scapegoat for the loss of six hundred lives. The warnings hadn't been urgent enough. The information hadn't been explicit enough. The fact remains, however, that repeated, insisted warnings were issued, in plenty of time. Those who heeded the warnings, survived.

R. W. Gray, in charge of the Weather Bureau office in Miami, wrote of a 1926 hurricane:

"The intensity of the storm and the wreckage that it left can not be adequately described. The continuous roar of the wind; the crash of falling buildings, flying debris and plate glass; . . . the terrifically driven rain that came in sheets as dense as fog; the electric flashes from live wires have left the memory of a fearful night in the minds of the many thousands that were in the storm area."

And the thousands who lived through that Miami hurricane, who saw the fury of Carol, Edna, Hazel, Audrey and dozens of others equally as terrifying, and fight today to live down their fearful memories—they are the lucky ones. For thousands of others throughout this century alone, there has been a last glimpse of falling ruin, a last clutch at a piece of floating debris, a last gasp of life, and then—nothing.

CHAPTER FOUR

Flood

"One moment the house was intact with seven adults and two children within its walls; seconds afterwards it was gone, and of the nine people only one survived. This was Mr. Tom Floyd, aged 63 years. He remembers his son's last words: 'We must get mother out,' and then seemed to be going down into a pit of water. He remembers, too, being siphoned upwards, and grabbing some masonry which proved to be the back of where his house had been. Regaining his feet, he found himself in the roadway in front of the cottages, and then, being forced along by the rushing water, he was caught by his daughter standing at her door a few yards along. Another astounding fact is that Floyd's dog, Tim, a four-year-old Cairn terrier, also in the room with them when the building collapsed, had got to the same refuge ahead of him. With the terrific rush of water outside, the depth of that gorge and the debris being carried along, it is nothing short of a miracle that either master or dog survived."

Thus Eric R. Delderfield records, in *The Elements Rage*, his interview with Mr. Thomas Floyd, a survivor of a disastrous inland flood which occurred during the night of August 15, 1952, in North Devon, England, at and around the seaside town of Lynmouth.

Floyd's house was on the road between Lynmouth and the edge of Exmoor, and in normal times the West Lyn River flows near by, 30 feet below the road level. At 9:30 Friday evening, Fred Floyd, the son, looked out and saw that the river was level with the house, and steadily rising. He and his father tried to rescue his mother from the downstairs bedroom, but it was too late. A wall of water strewn with debris hit the house and it disintegrated. All nine people inside were swept into the flood.

The Lynmouth flood occurred after a rainfall of twenty-four hours which poured 9.1 inches of rain on the area. Such rainfall has been exceeded only four times in the 100 years during which official records have been kept in Great Britain. An ordinary steady rain for twenty-four hours will deposit less than one inch in a rain gauge. Nine inches in the gauge represents more than half a million tons of rain per square mile. Dur-

69

ing one hour alone, the fall was about four inches.

When the rain began, the ground was already water-logged and a fairly shallow layer of rock prevented underground runoff. The East and West Lyn Rivers and their tributaries fall 1,500 feet through gorges into Lynmouth in less than four miles. These conditions combined to create the steady buildup of water that flooded Lynmouth so disastrously. At times the wall of water that raced down the gorges rose to more than 40 feet and moved at speeds up to 20 mph in its race to the sea.

The moving water gouged out rocks and boulders along the sides of the gorges, some of which weighed in excess of 15 tons. By the time the flood waters reached the town, telegraph poles, felled trees, uprooted trees and automobiles were added to the mass of boulders tumbling together in a marauding mass, adding to the lethal force of the flood.

Structures that weren't disintegrated by the force of the moving water alone were weakened by the pounding of large debris.

Incredibly, each of the seventeen bridges in the four miles between Exmoor and Lynmouth gave way to the debris-strewn flood, adding its own weight and bulk to the mess. Occasionally, the mass would jam together to form a temporary dam, only to be eroded by the tons of water behind it and to surge forth again to renewed destruction.

In addition to wrecking the sewerage system and water mains, the massive flood gouged out deep gullies along the soft earth of road verges, some of them as deep as twenty feet.

The debris left behind when the flood waters receded included some 200,000 cubic yards of silt, mud, gravel and stones, in some places piled 25 feet high. Thousands of tons of rocks and boulders, immense iron girders and sections of bridge, were inextricably woven in with the bodies of birds, fish, animals, and most horribly, people.

Thirty-four men, women and children were dead. Ninety-three buildings had been destroyed, 28 bridges destroyed or badly damaged, and 132 vehicles totally destroyed.

The scene at Lynmouth, when the waters began to recede, closely resembled the aftermath of another flood that took place half a century before, although the scale was considerably different. Two thousand lives were lost in the Johnstown flood, when a series of unprecedented rains created a vast reservoir of water which broke through a dam above the city of Johnstown, Pennsylvania, on May 31, 1889, and an additional 967 people were never found. But the quality of the experience was much the same. As Peter J. Toner describes it in *Man Against Nature:*

"Saturday morning dawned clear and bright. Streams still swollen separated different parts of the town. How many bodies lay strewn among animal carcasses and the wreckage could only be conjectured. Those watching on the hillsides beheld one of the most devastating scenes in the annals of American disasters. The few buildings that still occupied their original sites were damaged almost irreparably.

". . . In the days that followed, appalling sights bore witness to the misery of the city's people. So ghastly had been the experiences of many survivors that they prayed for death as a surcease. Nearly everyone who survived had lost some relative or close friend in the flood. One unidentified woman had been killed while giving birth to a child."

At the scene of any natural disaster, human behavior runs the gamut from craven to heroic, and the scene at Johnstown was no exception, although there was great heroism displayed by many who took tremendous risks themselves in order to attempt the rescue of those less fortunate. In situations where death was inevitable, some of the rescuers noted that the doomed met their end with fortitude and grace, and few succumbed to hysteria or panic. One of the witnesses told of a family on a large raft, bravely singing "Nearer, My God, to Thee," as the raft swirled around on the water, crashed into a tree, and slowly sank, carrying its occupants to their death.

At Pittsburgh on Saturday morning a nineteenth-century Moses was recovered from the flood waters. A baby five months old had floated the entire distance from Johnstown to Pittsburgh on the detached floor of a house, and was still alive and lusty at his rescue. No one ever discovered who his parents had been.

The recovery, identification and burial of the corpses was a tremendous, monumental, horrible task. Many of the bodies were so inextricably bound with the wreckage that it took weeks to take an even approximate death toll. The estimate was that 2,200 persons had died. Toner's account goes on to describe the recovery of the bodies:

". . . A room in Alma Hall was set aside for the reception of articles that might lead to the identification of the dead and the missing. Scenes of indescribable grief took place in this room. A glimpse at some of the entries in the records:

". . . $25 found in black silk stocking with female foot.

"$7.04 found on male, light hair, about 150 lbs.

"Ring with initials F.M.-L.H.—woman about 55, hair partly gray, dress black.

"Foot of child burned at the bridge, slightly charred.

"Girl about 6 months old, dark hair, white dress, brown bib.

"Child, 6 years old, no means of identification.

"Upon such meager information thousands of survivors visited the morgues, searching for missing relatives and friends. One of every three victims buried was unidentified. Frequently the dead were labeled for the living."

Throughout the world floods are one of the grimmest reapers of life and property. They rival any other natural disaster as a major destroyer of the works of man. The two main types of flood are inundation from the sea and overflowing of inland waters. Inland floods are sometimes regular and predictable, such as in the case of the Nile, but the dangerous, sporadic floods following unusually heavy rainfall present the worst hazard.

The most violent sea flooding usually occurs in connection with storms, earthquakes or volcanic eruptions. Sometimes wind and tide combine to drive the sea far inland.

In England there have been great and disastrous floods recorded since the Middle Ages. But the European country which has suffered most from sea floods is Holland. The Dutch, throughout their history, have fought an endless battle with their ancient enemy, a battle which at times seems to have been nearly lost.

On December 14, 1287, the Zuider Zee area was inundated and 50,000 people were drowned. On November 18, 1421, the southwestern part of Holland was covered with flood waters which destroyed 72 villages and killed 10,000 people.

Throughout the centuries, the Dutch have been slowly building a stronger and more efficient set of defenses against the sea, and in 1953 it seemed as if those defenses had just about tamed the waters. But on the weekend of January 31 and February 1, there occurred in Holland one of the great floods of modern times, and in a few hours, a great deal of the progress of centuries was lost, swept away by an uncaring arm of the enemy sea.

On the morning of January 31, tremendous gale-force winds and driving rain swept down on the east coast of Scotland. They were the worst northerly gales ever recorded in the British Isles, with winds that at times reached over 100 mph. During the day, the wind driving along the North Sea pushed thousands of millions of tons of water to the south, causing a rise in the mean level of the North Sea of about two feet. Coastal surges caused by the rise in water level were funneling inexorably into the narrow passage between southeast England and southwest Holland.

At the same time, several other factors were beginning to influence the situation in a fatal combination. The Atlantic surge into the North Sea combined with a high tide. And to tip the scales toward disaster, an atmospheric depression occurred which lowered air pressure, causing a still further rise in the sea. On the east coast of England, low-lying land began to flood. Coastal defenses were either crumbled or disdainfully ignored as the surges breached them in 1,200 separate places from Yorkshire to Kent. Three hundred square miles of southeast England were flooded, as the sea penetrated inland in some places as far as ten miles.

Tides in some places reached a height of 31 feet. The high seas driven by hurricane-force winds devastated the land. At Wells-by-the-sea, a 160-ton vessel was deposited on the quay. Thirty-foot cliffs near Lowestoft were cut back 30 feet, and a nearby cliff seven feet high was cut back 86 feet. Dunes and walls were washed away, beaches scoured and buildings shattered. Although 32,000 people were evacuated from the area, 307 still died, caught in the inexorable advance of water. Millions of dollars worth of damage were done to houses and agricultural land.

On the other side of the North Sea, Holland was wallowing. The sea had struck its cruelest blow in centuries. The violent winds continued to blow for eight hours continuously. At high tide, the Dutch dykes trembled as the gathered waters battered against them, and then gradually, and then with increasing speed, they were breached.

There are three kinds of dykes in Holland. The first line of defense, the biggest and strongest dykes, are called "watchers." Backing them up are the "sleepers," acting as a second line of defense. Individual farms and fields are surrounded by the comparatively small last-ditch defense, the "dreamers." Most of the dreamers are strongly reinforced on the seaward side, but once the watchers were breached, the second two lines of defense stood little chance of withholding the onslaught. Once the first few trickles began to weaken them, the dykes were quickly overwhelmed.

The sea rose until it was level with the 10-foot high dykes, and then a sudden surge burst over 50 dykes in a moment and the combined waters of the Atlantic and the North Sea were upon the land. In that raging flood that destroyed half a million acres, 2,000 people were drowned.

There had been warnings the previous night, but very few people had evacuated then. And indeed, the Dutch Meteorological Institute said that probably no floods of such intensity had occurred in 400 or 500 years. The people of Holland had expected, with good reason, that their defenses would hold.

Once past the dykes, the water flowed inland for miles, flooding highways, destroying or marooning villages, crushing buildings and drowning livestock in tens of thousands. Although 72,-000 people were evacuated, the invading sea claimed 1,835 more lives in its inland flood.

Everywhere people were climbing to the top floors of their houses, and then to the attics, as the water mounted relentlessly. Huddling in the dark, they could hear it swishing closer and closer as furniture slammed against walls on the flooded floors below. People stranded in the congealing cold kept moving to keep from freezing. Those who made it to high ground were often unprotected from the knifing wind and bitter spray, many of them were only partly dressed and wet to the skin.

An official Dutch report on the flooded town of Kortgene described the scene:

"The faces of many people were so distorted with fear that people could hardly recognize each other. There were continuous shrieks from people drowning or nearly drowning. People were seen to perish and several dead bodies were lying along the dyke without any attention according to the instinct of 'first the living, then the dead.' A few children who had just come out of the water were so terror-stricken that they continued running madly although the dyke was strewn with hard objects."

At Kortgene, one hundred men stood for hours with their backs against the dyke, straining to brace it against the onwelling flood.

As morning broke over Holland, thousands of people were stranded in the tops of trees, or perched precariously on rooftops. People jammed together on small patches of high ground clutched each other to keep from falling into the water.

People drifting in small boats and rafts risked the danger of being swept into the open sea as they attempted to rescue the stranded thousands. The twisted corpses of cattle, pigs and people were already starting to smell as they drifted by on the water. That afternoon, the surge of high tide collapsed even more dykes, with additional hundreds drowned.

Although sea floods are extremely destructive, they are much less frequent than those floods, such as the Lynmouth and Johnstown disasters, which occur as a result of overflow of inland waters. In the United States alone, inland flood damage averages over 300 million dollars a year. In 1955, it was over a billion.

Rain, melted snow and ice, accidental damming of rivers through landslides and earthquakes, rivers changing course, accumulation of silt which causes buildup on river bottoms, and the bursting of river banks, dams and the containing walls of lakes and reservoirs can all act as causes for inland floods. In all but the most sudden and violent floods—such as those caused by the bursting of a dam—ground conditions contribute a great deal to the hazard. Surface already saturated, rocky ground and frozen ground can absorb little excess water, and thus the flooding spreads more easily along the surface.

Rain is the primary cause of most inland floods. Throughout the world, including the oceans, the average estimated rainfall annually is about 40 inches, but of course the extent of rainfall varies greatly from area to area. The official record for 24 hours in the British Isles is 11.0 inches, which fell on July 18, 1955 at Martintown, Dorset. Underlying chalk strata absorbed much of the water and prevented a catastrophic flood.

In the rainstorm at Lynmouth, the rainfall approached this record, but the waterlogged ground and rocky substrata prevented absorption, and conditions combined to produce the devasting flood. Rainfall alone does not necessarily guarantee a flood, and usually other conditions in combination with rainfall are responsible.

Cloudburst and terrain sometimes combine to produce "flash floods," particularly in the southwestern United States. When heavy rain suddenly falls over a small area, draining into steep valleys and gullies, sudden and sometimes catastrophic floods can result. In the great flash floods, the water scours the valleys, moving earth, vegetation, trees, rocks and other debris along in a choking torrent.

On July 29, 1883, a flood at Kanab, Utah, gouged out a huge, deep channel below the former bed of the creek. Bishop W. D. Johnson was an eyewitness, and his observations are recorded in

F. W. Lane's account *The Elements Rage:*
"The torrent of water in volume, rapidity and noise resembled the whirlpool rapids of Niagara. Whole portions of soil with willows standing erect came floating down the stream; some of these floating islands were several rods in length by one or two wide. It beat everything I ever saw. It lasted for some seven or eight hours. The canyon was cut out at the old city dam some 50 odd feet down and 16 rods wide. The canyon is so changed you would not know it."

The greatest floods in North America occur in the area of the Lower Mississippi, where waters from 50 tributaries draining a million and a quarter square miles, flow into the greatest river in North America, the "Father of Waters," the Mississippi. At no time in recorded history have all the great tributaries of the Mississippi been in dangerous spate simultaneously. If this ever occurred, it could cause the greatest disaster in the history of the United States.

The floods that do occur are bad enough. In 1927, during the spring runoff, the waters in the Mississippi rose higher than those in some of its tributaries, and the backflow caused local waters to rise higher than their natural banks and artificial levees, flooding the land.

Frederick Simpich, who flew over part of the flooded area for the National Geographic Society, said:

"A vast sheet of water as yellow as the China Sea at the mouth of the Yangtze, stretches practically from southeast Missouri down to the Atchafalaya Basin of Louisiana. This sea is about 1,050 miles long and in places over 50 miles in width. Over 750,000 people normally live within its limits. Flying over it now in an airplane, you see the roofs of their houses, the smokestacks of their sawmills, their church steeples, the tops of their shade trees, and lines of telegraph poles sticking up from the water."

When the waters had receded and the mess had been cleared, 313 people were dead, and 637,-000 more displaced. Most deaths in floods of this kind come from the breaking of the levees that contain the Mississippi itself. Water flooding over the land moves at speeds of up to 15 and 20 miles per hour, and fleeing people are simply overwhelmed before they have time to escape.

The most disastrous of all floods occur in Asia, and it was there that evidence was found to substantiate the Biblical account of that great archetypal flood which inundated the land in Noah's day. Sir Leonard Woolley, excavating at Ur of the Chaldees in Lower Mesopotamia, found a deposit of water-laid clay 11 feet deep, indicating a flood of at least 25 feet in that spot. The evidence pointed to a sudden, devastating flood to which there is no parallel in later history.

In 1963, typhoons, rain and rivers changing course caused floods in East Pakistan that left three million people homeless and killed approximately 18,000 people.

The most flood-prone river in the world is the

Hwang Ho in China. This river, also called the Yellow River, is so named from the mixture of clay and sand which colors it with millions of tons of silt carried in its swift current from Inner Mongolia. In some stretches, 40 percent of the river's weight is silt, and each year the channel grows more shallow, rising an average of about three feet in a century.

In some 20 to 30 mile stretches, the slow rate of rise is stepped up tremendously, and the river bottom can rise up to six feet in a single year. In these stretches, the river can run up to 30 feet above the general level of the plain, and can flood way above that. The river presents a constant threat of danger and death to the 50 million farmers and peasants who live on the millions of square miles it nourishes. Those people, who have been flooded time and again, call the river "China's Sorrow."

Annual losses from flooding are worldwide and immense. A great deal can be accomplished through flood control projects to guard against the loss of life and property that a flood represents. However, from time to time, meteorologic and hydrologic conditions combine to produce floods of a magnitude with which even the most modern methods of control are incapable of dealing.

For most rivers, past floods may not be an accurate measure of ultimate flood potentialities, and there can never be complete safety from the possibility of flood. Floods are as much a part of the landscape as hills and valleys, and the problem of devising controls to prevent damage absorbs much time, thought, energy and money each year.

Before the works of man began to change the natural landscape, flood waters from heavy rainfall or melting snow found their way to the sea in natural channels and over normal flood plains. Now the channels are restricted and constricted by bridge piers, concrete arch bridges, transportation, sewer outlets, pipelines and other obstructions. The flood plains are occupied by factories, homes, waterworks, railroads, and highways. These conditions are evidence of a growing, prosperous nation, but at the same time they inevitably increase the potential for violent damage and loss of life.

The kind of planning and development which might minimize the potential for flood damage in a given area is so complex that even the tremendous resources of the federal government have thus far been unequal to the task. And only when such planning takes place can thousands of people be even marginally safe from the devastating waters that can sweep away homes, property and lives in a single thrust.

CHAPTER FIVE

Avalanche

" . . . Suddenly the mountain seemed to sway, and a quiver ran through the rocks. I clung for one brief moment of agony to the face of the cliff. And then suddenly a vast block, which must have been about ten feet high and several feet thick, separated itself from the face, heeled over on top of me and carried me with it into space. I turned a somersault, struck the cliff some distance below, bounded off once again and, after crashing against the ridge two or three times, landed on a sloping ledge about seven feet broad. The thunder of the rocks . . . showed how narrow had been my escape.

"I had fallen a distance which Lindsay estimated at a hundred feet. It was not a sliding fall, for except when I struck and rebounded I was not in contact with the ridge. The fall was long enough for me to retain a very vivid memory of the thoughts which chased each other through my brain during those few crowded seconds. I can still feel the clammy horror of the moment when the solid mountain face trembled below me, but the fall, once I was fairly off, blunted the edge of fear. My emotions were subdued, as if I had been partially anaesthetized. I remember vividly seeing the mountains upside down after my first somersault and that I was still falling. I remember making despairing movements with my hands in a futile attempt to check my downward progress.

"The chief impression was a queer feeling that the stable order of nature had been overturned. The tranquil and immobile hills had been startled into a mood of furious and malignant activity, like a dangerous dog roused from a peaceful nap by some inattentive passerby who has trodden on him unawares. And every time I struck the cliff only to be hurled downwards once again, I felt like a small boy who is being knocked about by a persistent bully—'Will he never stop? . . . surely he can't hit me again . . . surely he's hurt me enough.'

"When at last I landed, I tried to sit up, but fell back hurriedly on seeing my leg. The lower part was bent almost at right angles. It was not merely broken, it was shattered and crushed."

These eloquent words describe the experience of Arnold Lunn, an accomplished skier and mountaineer who is one of the few climbers who have ever been caught in a rock avalanche and lived to tell of it. The avalanche in which Lunn was injured occurred in Wales in 1909, and his eyewitness account is recorded in *Nature on the Rampage.*

Rock avalanches, rockslides and landslides are quite rare compared to snow avalanches, but they are potentially the most dangerous slides of all. Some of the worst of these tremendous rock falls have occurred in the same kind of country in which snow avalanches occur during winter snow storms. In Switzerland, on several occasions a large part of a whole mountain has fallen, crushing a town or village out of existence in moments. One of the earliest recorded avalanches of this type occurred at Plurs, Switzerland, on September 4, 1618. Nearly half the side of a mountain fell, obliterating the town of Plurs and bringing death to every one of the town's 1,500 inhabitants. Only four Plurs residents were left alive after the slide, and they had all been away from town when the rock avalanche occurred.

On September 2, 1806, one side of the Rossberg in the Alps collapsed, traveling swiftly across a valley and engulfing four villages. Over 500 people were killed, and the valley floor was raised by more than 100 feet when the dust from the rock fall had cleared.

Another Swiss rock avalanche took place on

September 11, 1881, near the village of Elm. This was one of several in which carelessness on the part of mining engineers could be traced as a direct cause of disaster. Above the village, overshadowing it ominously, was the Plattenbergkopf, part of the outer buttressing of a huge mountain mass, the Glarner Alpen. Halfway up the slope, mining operations had undermined the great rock mass, and occasional sporadic rock falls had threatened the village before. But no one heeded those harbingers of catastrophe.

On September 11, a heavy rain fell, and rocks bounced down on the village more heavily than usual. Still no one sensed that the mountain was about to move. Sightseers watched as part of the east side of the Plattenbergkopf broke away, and rocks fell almost at the feet of some of the onlookers. No one was hurt. Seventeen minutes later a larger mass fell from the west side of the mountain. By now the villagers were beginning to feel alarm, and many gathered on the hillside opposite the collapsing mountain. As they watched, the rocks groaned and rumbled with the strain.

The two large rock falls that had already crumbled into the valley had left the top of the Plattenbergkopf teetering on a tiny neck of rock. After only four minutes of balancing, millions of tons of rock began to hurtle down.

The huge avalanche fell as far as the quarry which had caused it, and then shot off across the valley, covering about a mile in less than half a minute. The town of Elm was completely annihilated, and half of another village was destroyed.

A great wind preceded the avalanche, whirling people into the air, uprooting trees and lifting houses from their foundations. A few houses were carried whole out of the path of the avalanche by the wind, but most bent, shook and broke up like paper boxes.

Flying rocks crushed people into red streaks, killing many instantly. Abruptly, the avalanche came to a stop. A tremendous roar filled the valley, gradually dying away into silence. The survivors stood stunned for a moment, and then the wailing began from the section of the village that was left. People began to run wildly about in all directions, but there was nothing they could do.

One hundred and fifty men, women and children were buried under ten million cubic yards of rock, and a million square yards of green fields were buried under a solid gray carpet of rock.

Although rock avalanches have been among the most devastating of all types of slides, by far the most common slide phenomenon has as its chief component one of the most beautiful and potentially deadly of all nature's creations—the snowflake. Snowflakes are composed of bunches of individual snow crystals. Single crystals fall comparatively rarely, except in very cold regions such as the Antarctic. Usually the lower air is relatively warm, and the rays of individual crystals stick to each other. Snow is the crystallization of water vapor in the air into geometrical forms. Snow is quite different from frozen rain, which produces ice pellets. Snow crystals form around a solid nucleus composed of smoke and dust over civilized areas and pollen, vegetable matter, grains of earth mud and salt over remote areas and over the sea. The crystals form in a variety of shapes—hexagons, needles, bullets, cones, and rods—due to varying atmospheric conditions. They are the units of which all snow is composed, and their properties under given conditions are an important factor in understanding the origin of snow avalanches.

When snow first falls, the snow cover contains a large proportion of air. After it falls, the snow begins to undergo a series of changes, passing through several stages as it converts into water or glacial ice. As the snow compacts its sheer weight can be a danger to buildings. On February 28, 1959, at the Listowel Arena, near Toronto, Ontario, the roof and walls of the ice rink collapsed from the weight of snow while a hockey game was being played. Eight people were killed, and many more were injured.

The most familiar form of avalanche is caused by massed snow. Early attempts to categorize avalanches made a distinction between the ground avalanche of wet snow which slides over the ground and carries much earth and debris with it, and the powder avalanche which consists of dry, powdery snow. However, some avalanches are a combination of these two plus other types, and many are too complex to fit in any classification. Whenever a mass of snow which has been stable on a mountainside loses its hold and hurtles down, an avalanche has occurred. There are many different circumstances in which this can occur, and various factors can influence the severity of the avalanche including irregularities formed by rocks or mounds which might arrest the avalanche's forward movement and the structure of the snow covering itself.

When a mass of snow is almost ready to fall, very small disturbances can trigger it into plummeting action. In the Rocky Mountains, train vibrations start many avalanches. Even the passage of a small animal, such as a fox, can set an avalanche in motion. Although most winter seasons produce only sporadic avalanches in the great snow regions of the world, sometimes a set of circumstances combine that can produce a series of avalanches terrifying in their devastation. The snow season of 1950-1951 was such a winter, with a series of avalanches throughout the whole Alpine area that left no valley untouched.

The early weeks of the winter were not particularly unusual, although the first snowfalls were about ten days earlier than average. In December, the snowfall was only about half of normal, although the weather was cold with very little sun. The later winter months would make up for a dry December with more than vengeance, producing from three to five times the average fall in a wide area of the Alps.

Towards the middle of January, an anticyclone built up over Spain, sending a stream of warm air northeastward toward the Alps. At the same time, cold air lay over the Balkans, Italy, Germany and the North Sea. The fronts of all these air masses congregated over the Alps. When the warm air from the south rose over the cold, the snow started. Between January 12 and 15th, wind and snow intensified over northeast Switzerland, and on the evening of the 15th, the first phase of a great blizzard began.

During the 16th, it snowed without letting up, and by the morning of the 17th, another two feet of snow glistened on top of the old layers. There was a brief break in the weather that morning, and then the blizzard began in earnest. By the morning of the 22nd, after five days and nights of continuous snow, the total snowfall in the area was more than nine and a half feet.

The cold of December had produced an unstable base layer of old snow, and the new tremendous fall was creating an ominous situation. By the 19th, it had become obvious that the situation was grave, and ski areas had been closed. But patrolmen had to protect the ski lifts and other installations which could be wiped out by the avalanche that was building.

High above Klosters, the newly built Gotschnagrat cable car was particularly threatened. The middle station of the cable car stood on almost flat ground at the foot of the spectacular Gotschnawang, a precipitous face which soared some 2,300 feet above the station. Stephen Hartmann, a patrolman for the entire Parsenn area which had been closed to skiers, was assigned to drop cans of explosive from the cable car at regular intervals to prevent a big avalanche from building up on the Wang.

Hartmann set out in the late afternoon with an employee of the cable car company, Christian Conrad, to drop his explosives. They were trying to reach Mast 7, the spot from where the explosives were to be dropped. Just before the cable car cabin reaches it there is a drop of several hundred feet on to the rock outcrops of the Wang below. Just at that point, the cabin swayed so violently in the gale that the traction cable jumped its rollers and the cabin was left dangling in space.

For four hours, Hartmann and Conrad hung helpless in the cabin, tossed about in the tremendous gale like a child's toy. The cabin swung wildly backward and forward, bouncing up and down on its support cable. The men inside were white with fear in an agony of suspense. At any moment during the four hours of their ordeal, the cable might dislodge and send them plummeting to the rocks. Outside, the snow storm was blinding and relentless. As night fell with a darkening of the raging blizzard, they realized that even if they didn't fall, they might freeze to death in the tiny cabin unless help came soon.

Christian Jost had rushed to Klosters to help in the rescue of the two men, and was inching toward them in an emergency car, an open cage exposed to the merciless storm. The dangers for Jost were even worse than for the two stranded men, but it was the only means of rescue. Jost gave telephone instructions to the men controlling the speed of the emergency car, and chose his moment very carefully. He managed to maneuver himself up to the main cabin, but both cabins were oscillating wildly. Hartmann and Conrad climbed across into the cage while the cabins tossed violently in the wind, a crossing only slightly less perilous than their precarious perch.

Their ordeal was one of many that night as the human population waited fearfully for the avalanches they were desperately trying to prevent.

Everyone who could possibly be evacuated down to Klosters had been bundled into the cable car and taken to that place of comparative safety, but at the middle station two cable car employees stayed behind to operate the machinery to get the last evacuee to the valley. Along with them was Eugen Unold, another *Parsenndienst* patrolman, and awaiting Unold was a special grim and vital task. Every hour throughout the night, Unold was to brave the storm with a can of explosive, fling it as far towards the Gotschnawang as possible, and rush back into the building and into the cellar while the long fuse burned. It was hoped that the explosions might bring the avalanche down while it was still relatively harmless.

Hour after hour, Unold went out into the storm with his charge, flung it boldly toward the mountain and detonated it. The explosions were heard several miles down the valley, an hourly punctuation of the vigil that many kept that night. But no avalanche followed the detonations. With each failure, the anxiety of the waiting men grew.

In the small hours of the storm, there was a sudden series of eery flashes outside the windows of the middle station. To the haggard men inside, it seemed as if the end of the world had come. Later they discovered that the wind had short-circuited some high-tension electricity cables just below the station.

At 6:00 A.M. Unold flung another charge toward the mountain, with yet another failure. Then just before 6:30, the men heard the terrible rushing noise of avalanching snow, drowning out even the howl of the shrieking wind. As they shouted warnings to each other, Unold saw the telephone leave the table and fly up to the ceiling in that blast of air which precedes an avalanche. Then the lights went out and the avalanche slammed into the frail middle station, tearing off two walls of the building. The roof was lifted off and dropped again onto the rooms, and in the few seconds it was off, the rooms had been half-filled with snow.

The three men at the middle station survived. Not far away, there were many others who weren't as lucky. The terrible winter of 1950-51 had just begun.

On the morning of January 19, a roadworker, Burtel Gross, had been clearing snow from the Ofen Pass near Zernez. An avalanche carried him away. By middle afternoon a rescue party had been raised. Christian Golay, a Pontresina chemist, was in charge of the rescue. Realizing that the rescuers were threatened by secondary avalanches on the same track, he posted three observers at the edge of a steep gully, with horns so they could warn the others if avalanches broke away.

About 45 minutes after the start of the rescue, a group of five men and an avalanche dog found Gross near the bottom of the gully. Three of the men began artificial respiration while the other two began to fix a rope down the rock ledge for the descent of the rescuers higher up. But Golay ordered the men above to detour through a wood, a cautious decision that had fortunate consequences for the detouring men.

Only moments before reinforcements reached the men in the gully, the horns blared and another avalanche roared down the gully. An observer saw the men in its path picked up and flung like puppets onto the far bank of the stream that cuts through the bottom of the gully. A pall of snow-dust from the powder avalanche then obscured the view.

Now the search for the original victim, the five rescuers and the dog began. By nightfall, with the storm still raging at full force, none of the victims had been found.

Late that night, the exhausted searchers were about to turn their task over to relief forces when another powder avalanche roared down the track. It rushed through the night and burst on the scene, slamming against the slope on the far side of the stream and spreading out at the bottom of the gully. Ernst Thut, at the rear of the retreating group of rescuers, was picked up, pulled several meters toward the avalanche, and quickly buried under tons of snow and debris. Thut was found an hour and a half later by an avalanche dog, but more than three hours of artificial respiration could not revive him.

The operation was then called off, and the spiritless rescuers made their way to Zernez. In the gully behind them they left seven dead men, all but one of them married and with families. The search was resumed a few days later, but the bodies were not completely exhumed from their icy tomb until the middle of June. The avalanche snow had frozen so hard that dynamite and pickaxes had to be used to locate and extricate the bodies.

Ernst Thut, the last man to die in the rescue, had lived in a nearby village, Zuoz, which in its turn would suffer an avalanche scourge. Zuoz is an old village, lying between the outlets of two large avalanche gullies, the Val Buera, and the Val d'Urezza. For centuries avalanches have poured down those gullies, and the village system of self-protection had evolved and been officially adopted in 1946, when the village elders decided to use an avalanche committee and a mortar crew to shoot explosives at the mountain and bring down avalanches in both gullies before they could reach dangerous proportions.

On the morning of January 20, all the members of the avalanche committee were in the rescue party out of Zernez, and the resulting complications in terms of authorizing the mortar crew delayed the explosives until late afternoon. A few minutes after four, the mortar officer took his position on the outskirts of the village and fired the fateful bomb into the whirling snow. Waiting tensely for its detonation, the mortar officer heard only an eery humming and whining. An instant later he and his two helpers were struck by snow. One man was flung into a shed where he landed on the back of a cow; another was buried up to the neck; and the mortar officer was buried completely. He was found after a few minutes, but his face had already begun to change color.

The single mortar bomb had released avalanches in the Val d'Urezza, in the Val Buera, and on the Albanas slope directly above the village. Several houses destroyed by the Albanas avalanche were unevacuated, and five people died. Dozens of buildings in the village were destroyed.

In that northeast corner of Switzerland, avalanches throughout the winter fell by the thousand. More than 600 of them did damage to life and property. Fifty-four people were killed. One of the main railways serving the area had more than 100 avalanches on its line, one of which carried an entire railway station building onto the tracks and buried six people.

In Andermatt, in central Switzerland, that winter brought a war of nerves unprecedented in the history of the village. During the 19th, the people of the village heard the news of the rescue disasters in the Val Barcli. Then news reached Andermatt of an avalanche that had destroyed 14 buildings in the village of Realp, only five miles away. During that day, the 20th, three avalanches fell into the village itself, but all who were caught in them survived. Tension in the village was rising, and everywhere people were discussing the advisability of evacuation. At early afternoon, no one had yet decided to evacuate.

Just before 1:45, Stephen Theuss and Wilhelm Lutz, tenants in a large subdivided house, were cleaning snow off the roof of the house. Lutz heard an indescribable noise, a mixture of roaring, humming, hissing and whining. In the next instant he saw a dark, swirling mass coming straight at him. He kicked in the window near where he was standing and was halfway through the frame when he had the impression of the roof closing in from both sides. Then he felt himself lifted up, and set down again a couple of seconds later.

He fought his way out of the window frame, in which he was still sitting, pushed up through a few inches of snow and found himself some 60 yards from where he had been a few seconds earlier.

More than 300 people worked to uncover survivors, but they found only bodies. In the course of the afternoon they dug out the bodies of Stephan Theuss, his wife, and two children, aged 15 and 6. Five other people were still missing. While the rescue operations were going on, still more avalanches descended on the village. Eventually the threat to the 300 rescue workers forced a halt in the rescue operations. All that day and night, into the small hours of January 21st, avalanches continued to fall on the hapless village, claiming more and more lives of men, women and children. Bodies of Wilhelm Lutz's wife and 3-year-old son were found. More and more bodies were unearthed from the freezing snow.

In a secluded and beautiful valley some 30 miles east of Andermatt lies the tiny village of Vals. Between January 17th and 20th, nearly four feet of snow fell on Vals, and on the morning of the 20th, the storm intensified. People began discussing the possibility of avalanche. That night there was an emergency meeting to discuss evacuation, but even while the meeting was being conducted, the avalanche struck. Almost all of the village was obliterated by a jumble of snow and the village was in chaos.

The first person to be recovered from the avalanche was nine-year-old Franz Casanova, who had been hurled out of his bed and shot through a first-floor window to land in the street under some timbers.

He was returned unhurt to his father, but sixteen hours later the boy's mother was found with her six-month-old daughter dead in her arms. Eight hours later the mother died from her injuries. The dead bodies of two older daughters were found the next day.

From the same house the dead body of Philip Peng was removed after a few hours, and his injured wife Franziska was found after 16 hours, lying below Frau Casanova. The two women had been able to talk to each other during their ter-

rible ordeal of burial, but only Frau Peng recovered. The bodies of her two small children
were not found for two and a half days. From
the ground floor of the house, a husband and wife
were saved, but their three-month-old and eigh-
teen-month-old children were both found dead.

In another house an entire family was found
dead. All over the village, families had been partially destroyed, and rescuers were still claiming
bodies from the wreckage three days later.

In that January period of 1951, there were more
than 1,100 avalanches in Switzerland alone that
caused damage to life and property in the valleys, and probably thousands more that came
down harmlessly in unpopulated areas. By January 22nd, some 240 people had already been killed
in the Alps, and the population was still searching for bodies, still examining wreckage, grief-
stricken and unbelieving, when two weeks later,
it began to snow again.

By the time that winter was over, 279 people
had lost their lives in the Alps, and a further 285
had been severely injured. Livestock had been
decimated, much of the wild life of the area was
wiped out, and 2,500 buildings were either destroyed or damaged. About 15,000 acres of timber
had been ripped out.

Plans were made to build defenses against the
possibility of future avalanches in the coming
years, and to replant the destroyed woodland, at
a cost of more than a million dollars but those
cost estimates proved to be inadequate. Almost
every village in the Alps built, or is still building,

a defense system to prevent the recurrence of another year like 1951.

According to the Swiss Snow and Avalanche Research Institute, the avalanches of 1951 had been the worst since 1720. It was the greatest avalanche disaster on record.

Compared with other natural hazards, the losses caused by avalanches are not great. These small losses are primarily due to the fact that the majority of avalanches come down in uninhabited regions, where loss of life and property is small. But for the people who lived through the winter of terror in 1951, those losses have changed the face of the land and the course of lives beyond recall.

CHAPTER SIX

Forest Fire

"That Sunday was noticed as a chilly day, though the atmosphere was still and filled with smoke. The smoke created no alarm, as the smoldering fires in the pineries about sufficiently accounted for it. Towards evening the smoke increased while the chilliness in the atmosphere perceptibly abated and early in the evening gave way to occasional hot puffs from the burnt districts.

"Sunday evening, after church, the town was quiet; the smoke from the fires in the region had become so thick as to be stifling and hung like a funeral pall over everything.

"Soon after eight in the evening, with the

warmth of the atmosphere increasing and the smoke almost suffocating in its intensity, a sullen rumbling began to be heard far away in the southwest. At half-past eight the far-off rumbling had increased to a steady roar, like distant thunder or the coming of heavy freight trains at full speed. Men felt their way through the smoky streets and congregated at the hotels and other places of resort, and discussed the strange sounds. Anxious mothers nervously and hesitatingly put their little ones to bed, and then peered out in the dismal streets to see what they could see.

"Nine o'clock came, and with it an alarming increase of the unknown sound, which now resembled the roar of a dozen freight trains at full speed.

"Suddenly there was a cry of fire sounding through the smoke-beclouded streets, and men rushed hither and thither through the impenetrable blackness, rubbing their eyes for sight, and stumbling against each other as they ran. But no fire was found, though the search extended out of the village and into the edge of the woods.

"Scarcely had the first alarm subsided when the cry was raised again, in another quarter, and the blind running and stumbling was renewed. While this confusion was at its height, and while most of the men were away from their houses, angry puffs of almost burning heat came sweeping through the town while, at quick intervals, a frightful glare penetrated the smoke from the southwest.

"Mothers caught their children from their beds,

and hastily dressed them. A cry of terror filled the town. Men, women and children, horses, dogs, oxen, swine, fowls—everything that had life ran wildly to escape the impending destruction.

"Then, with the howling of a tornado a storm of fire which rained down on the doomed village like flaming missiles shot from unseen artillery. The heavens rained fire on every head as if to consume the whole earth.

"Houses crumpled like paper, and flaming roofs were borne away like gigantic sparks upon the fiery gale. People threw themselves on the ground and perished where they fell. The storm of falling cinders was followed quickly by a continuous blaze that licked up everything with which it came in contact.

"Some, who had sought refuge in the river, saved themselves by keeping their bodies submerged, only raising their heads at intervals to gasp for breath. Many were drowned in the effort to escape burning, while others, who sought to catch breath, inhaled livid flame, and perished. Even the fishes were reached by some mysterious agency, so that the next day hundreds of them were found floating dead."

That was how it was in Peshtigo on the evening of October 8, as a violent gale sprang up suddenly sweeping the previously smoldering fires of an unusually dry season through the woods of Michigan and Wisconsin. The story is told by a newspaper reporter who covered the great fire storms of 1871 that followed a fourteen-week drought. Another correspondent had a view of the tremendous fire from a passenger boat on one of the lakes. His report, also recorded in *Great True Stories of Tragedy and Disaster*, gives some idea of the range of the fire which devastated Peshtigo:

"The fire on the east side of the Bay extended in an almost unbroken line from the eastern shore of Lake Winnebago to the northern extremity of the Eastern Peninsula, a distance of 150 miles. So deep and dismal was the darkness caused by the immense volume of smoke that the sun was totally obscured for a distance of two hundred miles. . . . The air was red with burning fragments carried from Peshtigo and other places along the shore, a distance of fifty miles."

The population of Peshtigo, about 2,500 before the fire, was ravaged. Seven hundred and fifty were dead in the small town. Morning found hundreds of survivors, many of them badly burned, wet through and miserable, still crouching in the water of the river. The village was a blackened ruin with not a house left standing, and the ground was still too hot to walk on. Peshtigo suffered the worst damage of that huge two-state fire, but the list of villages burned out includes dozens, and many isolated farms were burned and their owners perished.

A farmer named James Langsworth lived near St. Charles in Saginaw County, on a ninety-acre farm. On the Sunday of the big fire, he was alone; his wife and children were visiting friends in Canada. On Sunday morning, clouds of smoke began to drift across the farm, darkening the sky and causing terrible suffering to Langsworth's animals. On Sunday afternoon he turned his cow and several head of young stock loose. He never saw them again.

At that time, he figured the fires were burning about a mile away from him. He was confident that a partially dried-up swamp between the farm and the edge of the forest would stop the fires if they turned in his direction. That night he sat up in his farmhouse in a terrible vigil, waiting to see what the fire would do. About midnight the wind changed, and he began to hear the roar of the flames in the distance. All night long he listened to the crashing of the big trees as they toppled over. At daybreak there was hardly any light, only thick billowing smoke and the roar of the flames getting steadily louder. Langsworth judged that the fire must have eaten its way around the edge of the swamp and was on its way to devour the farm. He decided to flee.

While he was tying up a few valuables in a blanket, a huge flame shot up from his barn and haystacks, and a rain of burning twigs and branches swept in through the door of the farmhouse. He dropped the bundle and began his run for his life.

He took a wagon road that led from his farm to the village, stifling in smoke, unable to swallow with his throat parched dry and his lungs knifed with pain. He stumbled forward, trying to keep ahead of the fire, but another fire jumped the road in front of him, cutting off what seemed to be his only means of escape.

Fire was on three sides of him now, burning in huge sheets of flame. He turned to his left, where the way was still clear, falling and stumbling forward, jumping to avoid burning cinders, and several times leaping with his arms around his head through small surface fires. Finally he reached a gang of men constructing a fire line around the village of St. Charles. His clothes were almost burned away and he was covered with blisters, but he survived. He had lost everything he had in the fire, except his life. There were others who were not so fortunate.

On one lonely, outlying farm, the Charles Lamp family tried to carry some of their household goods away in a wagon before the fire caught up with them, but they didn't make it. Lamp's wife and five children all died in the flames, and Lamp himself was horribly burned. Another farm family named Lawrence was wiped out where they tried to take refuge in a large clearing.

One large farming family of seventeen members was almost wiped out, with twelve family members burned to death. A neighboring family and a visiting family with three children were all killed.

A visitor from Detroit, Mr. Brady, was staying in the village of White Rock, Huron County, on that Sunday night when the fire swept in on the village. The villagers tried to fight it, to no avail, and finally fled to the lake, where they were in the water for eight hours, watching as the fire destroyed their entire village. After the fire had passed by, the villagers emerged exhausted from the water and found that no food or shelter was available for miles around. They were finally rescued by a Lake steamer, which also collected ravaged inhabitants of several nearby towns.

Near Gardner, Wisconsin, three brothers owned a sawmill and lumber business in a small hamlet which numbered about seventy people. They had dug and burned a fire line nearly a mile wide all around the settlement, believing it would surely make them impregnable. It wasn't enough. When the gale hit the forest, sending hundred-foot-high flames roaring through the trees, a huge rain of burning fragments came down on the settlement, igniting the buildings and scattering the people in panic. Many of them fought each other for refuge in a tiny well. Others struggled to gain possession of a small pit dug in a potato patch. The few who ran into the woods away from the fire survived. Sixty-one of them, maddened and confused by the fire, died in their pitiful strongholds.

The kind of confusion and near-insanity that struck the inhabitants of the little settlement near Gardner occurred in many other circumstances during the same great fire. The story of what happened to one member of a French family of settlers in north Wisconsin is another case of insanity induced by the confusion of the flames, and is scarcely to be rivaled in horror by any other tale of the fire.

The family consisted of Mr. and Mrs. Mechand, their son Louis, aged six, and Mrs. Mechand's mother, who was somewhat mentally deficient.

On the morning of October 11, while they were breakfasting, a neighbor warned them that the forest fires were burning very close. After deliberating about evacuation all day, the neighbor again looked in and told them the fire was advancing at a terrible speed, and they had better flee. The family left the house and ran for three miles. Mrs. Mechand was carrying Louis, while her husband struggled with her mother, sometimes dragging the old woman along as she tried to break away from him and run into the flames. Finally, having outrun the fire by a good mile, they paused to rest, exhausted. Mrs. Mechand put the boy down, and her husband released the mother. After a few minutes, the old woman ran away. Before they could stop her, she was lost in the trees and smoke. Mr. Mechand ran after her. Mrs. Mechand, terrified, put the boy down and ran after him, leaving the child.

After a minute or two, she suddenly realized she was lost. She had no idea where the child was, where her husband was. As Mrs. Mechand tells it:

"Madly I tried to retrace my steps, but there was nothing to guide me, no path, no blazes on the trees. The wind shook the trees and almost bent them double: the sultry air filled with smoke and all the horrors of my condition made me frantic. I rushed about helplessly, crying and screaming, 'Louis! Louis! Mother!' "

After fifteen minutes of panic-stricken search, Mrs. Mechand found her son, but not her husband or her mother. By this time the fire was getting close, and the air was filled with whirling firebrands. Mrs. Mechand and the boy ran on, resting in a clearing, and then continuing their mad flight. After dark, they were caught up in a stampede of wild animals. Mrs. Mechand describes it:

"I heard the mingled gnashing and hoarse barking, which I instantly recognized as that of wolves, and I had scarcely time to snatch up Louis and run behind a tree before they rushed by me. They did not stop for an instant: and when they had passed there came in their track a herd of deer, uttering cries that seemed almost human in their intense agony. The stampede lasted a good ten minutes, and when it was over I saw the woods already burning and felt the terrible heat on my face.

"I turned and fled in the wake of the deer and the wolves. My shoes were stripped from my feet and my ankles were torn and bloody. Finally I sank to the ground with the boy in my arms. I know nothing of what passed then till I was rudely shaken by the shoulder and heard a wild gibbering laugh. I opened my eyes, and above me stood my mother with a drawn knife in her hand.

". . . I sprang to my feet and cried: 'Mother, what are you doing? Do you want to kill me and Louis?'

" 'Kill you! Yes. Why wait? The Lord calls and the devil drives. He has let loose his imps against the world. The trees are falling in the forest: all hell's demons pull them down with hooks of fire. I will kill you: would you burn to death? Come,

110

let us go,' and she seized Louis, while the knife gleamed in her hand.

"I sprang at her with all my strength and struggled with her. Torn, bleeding as I was, the thought of the child gave me strength. I overpowered the mad woman: I seized her throat and would have strangled her. Her insanity had almost made me mad.

"But then I thought, she was my mother, and my hand was stayed, and when she rose to her feet all her wildness was gone and in its place had returned that calmness, almost imbecility, which had characterized her for the last few years. She was ready and willing to do all I told her, but I kept the knife in my hand.

"The woods were now not as intolerably hot. The wind had dropped, and a light rain was falling. We went on for an hour or two longer, and then lay down in a hollow and fell asleep. When we awoke men were round us who gave us food and shelter, and as soon as we were able we went to Green Bay. There I soon recovered from the sickness and terror of that dreadful night. My mother continues in the same state of imbecility, which the doctor says will soon become complete dementia. Louis was not long in recovering. I have heard nothing of my husband."

Thus Mrs. Mechand fought successfully for her life and won, and yet found the pattern of her life unalterably changed by the great disaster. Even the survivors of such an experience carry marks and scars which the years cannot erase.

In Marinette, teams of men hauled water for

fourteen hours while other teams drenched the ground and trees. The fire swept on past the village and obliterated several neighboring hamlets, but Marinette was saved. It soon became a hospital center, where there were several patients recovering from attempted suicide in addition to the many persons actually injured in the fire. Others did commit suicide when the flames cut them off. One man killed his whole family before committing suicide himself. A wealthy farmer shot all his horses before he shot himself.

Many of the injured were blinded, some temporarily, others for life. Almost every patient at the Marinette hospital had lost all or most of his family. One old man had lost his wife, daughter, son and eight grandchildren.

In an area of the peninsula between Saginaw Bay and Lake Huron, twenty-three towns and villages were burned out and eighteen partially destroyed. Hundreds of isolated farms were blackened ruins. Thousands of animals died pathetically in the flames, thousands of people were left ruined and homeless, and more than 1,500 men, women and children had lost their lives.

Up until twenty years ago, the record of forest fires in Wisconsin was one of the worst in the northern United States. Tremendous fires swept huge areas of the state in several years following that devastation of 1871. There were fires equally bad in 1880, 1891, 1894, 1897, 1908, 1910, 1923, 1931 and 1936. Almost every year, at least five hundred thousand acres of Wisconsin timberland

1972: driven by gale winds, a line of fire creeps across a ridge to threaten Big Sur.

Out of control, this California fire advances. The toll: $50,000,000 worth of timber.

The 1923 Tokyo quake twisted some buildings into scrap, leveled others to the ground.

Mexico City, 1957: earthquake victims included small children and an expectant mother.

30,000 perished, and an entire town was obliterated, in the 1902 eruption of Mt. Pelée.

Anchorage, Alaska, 1964: the earth opens to swallow
a whole city block as a quake rocks the permafrost.

1960: a second tidal wave hit Hawaii, triggered by
a big earthquake thousands of miles away in Chile.

Hilo, 1946: a lone human (arrow) stands helpless in the path of a towering tidal wave.

was burned. Some years the figures rose to more than a million acres. All of the great recorded fires are those that got out of control and swept through vast acreages before they burned themselves out. There were an additional almost continuous series of small fires that were unrecorded, but the cumulative destruction they did has been monumental.

In 1929, the state itself recognized some of the causes of devastating fires. Logging had been an important factor in denuding the landscape, and combined with fires that swept through carelessly logged forests, it had brought about a destruction that would not be easily rectified. However, the Wisconsin state legislature began to take steps to correct former logging practices and to develop a system of forest-fire prevention, detection and suppression that has helped to cut losses from fire in recent years. However a century of raging forest fires and almost equally raging logging operations has devastated one of the largest natural forests in the country.

The great fire of 1871 resulted in a tragic loss of life in epic proportions, and few fires since then have taken such a toll of human life. However, there have been many fires which have taken an equally tragic toll in wiping out all the life in billions of acres of timber. One such fire took place in western Oregon in 1933. The Tillamook fire, named for one of the Oregon counties through which it burned, destroyed half a billion feet of fine old timber, a figure probably not exceeded by any fire before or since. It was one of the greatest forest conflagrations of all time.

The fire began a little after one o'clock on the hot dry afternoon of August 14, 1933. The forest lookout perched on top of Saddle Mountain had been staring down at the thousands upon thousands of rolling acres of ancient Douglas fir that seemed to go on until the end of the world itself. At 1:15 that afternoon he saw the one thing he dreaded and feared the most—a billow of white smoke, rolling up out of Gales Creek Canyon.

The lookout reported the smoke by telephone to his warden at Forest Grove. At the same time, a lookout at Hoffman Station, ten miles northeast of the smoke, had also reported it. Within minutes, a crew of men were on their way.

That morning had opened hot and dry, and long before noon a brisk wind had played on much of western Oregon, including Gales Creek Canyon. The heat was so high, and humidity so low, that all major logging operations had been suspended at noon. All but one. One particular outfit went back to work after lunch, loading timber in a forest that had been dry for two months and was now like tinder.

In the process of hauling one huge log out of the woods, the lumbermen dragged it grindingly hard across a wind-felled cedar so old and dry that the grinding action acted as a primitive fire maker. Seconds after the huge log's passage, a thin puff of white smoke curled up from the cedar. Within only a few minutes, the smoke was thicker and the hook tender yelled, "Fire!"

That was the beginning. The logging crew in

Gales Creek Canyon and a hundred additional men fought the fire all that afternoon and made no headway. Shortly after six o'clock, another fire was reported raging miles south of the original blaze, a piece of it having leaped the intervening green miles on a stiff breeze. More truckloads of men were dispatched to the area from near-by camps and sawmills. They fought all night long, and made miles of fire line to contain the ground fire. Then the new blaze crowned—went up into the treetops and began to travel with the speed of the wind.

Hundreds of more men began to fight, and by Saturday night, August 19, it looked like the fire had been contained. Sunday morning the wind was down, but in the afternoon it rose rapidly and within half an hour most of the fire line had been obliterated. The flames crossed the lines two hundred feet above the earth. The fire raced on, headed toward two conservation camps which were quickly evacuated with only moments to spare.

The man on Saddle Mountain lookout who had originally reported the fire escaped down the side of the mountain only half an hour before the fire destroyed the lookout. More fire fighters poured into the area, and the village of Forest Grove began to look like a wartime camp. It was a war indeed, a war to save four centuries of trees. On Monday, it looked like the men were losing.

By Thursday, August 24th, 40,000 acres of timber had been burned over. The fire had been raging for eleven days. Humidity was rising, though, and the wind had died down again almost to nothing. It began to look as though the crisis had passed.

Then, during the night, the humidity plunged again, and a hot, dry east wind whipped a gust of trouble through the as yet unburned timber, growing stronger. Fire fighters, ranchers and their families quickly evacuated along the west front of the fire. One rancher was throwing belongings in a truck when heat from the oncoming fire began to melt the paint on the truck. He got out fast, passing herds of running deer on his way.

That day, the worst happened. The fire had blown up. Along a fifteen-mile front a wall of flame leaped through the tops of four-hundred-year-old trees. Fifty miles away in Portland, people marvelled at the huge motionless cloud that hung in the sky southwest of the city.

The huge mushroom of smoke hung in the sky for two days. The wind over the fire rose almost to hurricane force, uprooting giant firs before the flames could touch them. The ancient trees fell with huge booms which punctuated the thundering roar of the inferno. A rain of fire in the form of burning brands and hot ashes fell over the entire western portion of Oregon. The air over half the state was choked with thick gray smoke, and the roads were clogged with residents trying to get out, to get somewhere where they could breathe.

For forty miles along the Pacific shore, smoke and fire rolled out over the ocean, carrying blackened bits of debris far out to sea. The incoming tides pulled black twigs, branches and even whole treetops two feet deep for miles along the beaches.

August 24th was a black day for much of Oregon. Ten miles north of the Tillamook blaze, another fire burned out of control. Rising wind set spot fires all over the district. Once more, valiant fire fighters seemed to be bringing things under control, and then on Saturday, the betraying wind rose yet again, blowing with hurricane force for several hours, and the fire was wholly out of control.

Three thousand men working around the clock had almost no effect on the incredible Tillamook fire as it raged through the day and night. Only a wet, thick fog blanket rolling in from the coast put the fire on the ground.

In all that inferno, with thousands of men working to control the blaze, only one life was lost, and that not even by fire. Frank Palmer was killed instantly when a big fir, uprooted by the great wind, struck him down as he patrolled a section of the line.

But the gigantic fire destroyed twelve and a half billion feet of some of the best timber in the United States. It burned over 311,000 acres. The direct loss from the fire is staggering, but even it pales into insignificance when compared to the loss in future forests. Some parts of the burn have begun restocking themselves naturally, and will be ready for cutting again in about A.D. 2015, barring another disastrous fire. But thousands of acres were burned so savagely that no trees at all were left alive, and no seeds left unscorched on the forest floor.

Modern methods of fire control include an intensified effort to contain fires in their infancy through the use of smoke jumpers, trained airborne firefighters who are also expert parachutists. During the fire season of 1951, the Forest Service Parachute Loft at Missoula, Montana, dropped sixty-four men into the area of fires scattered over 25,000,000 acres in one day. The smoke jumpers are doing a magnificent job of containing small fires the instant they are spotted, before they can grow into a raging inferno like the one that ravaged the Tillamook area. However, the job of a smoke jumper is not without extreme hazards. In that same fire season of 1951, the Missoula station lost twelve men to a fire around Helena, Montana.

One smoke jumper from the Missoula station, Starr Jenkins, describes his philosophy of fire fighting in *Man Against Nature:*

" 'Separate the fuel from the fire'—the old simplicity-itself fire-fighting method of the Forest Service. It doesn't take water or chemicals or bombs or pumps or hoses, though all those things may help if available. All it takes in essence is men, enough men with tools, and lots of sweat and backbending and shiny places on the insides of thumbs. . . ."

118

It is another widely recognized truth that the main ingredient necessary for starting fires is also men.

CHAPTER SEVEN

Earthquake

"Some had gained the street and escaped the direct flames. Their bodies lay almost entire, but with cruel blisters. Theirs must have been a far greater agony than that of others whose remains are but charred fragments—perhaps just a bit of blackened skull visible amid piled-up bricks and twisted wire and shop goods. How many are buried in that tangled mass? No one will ever know. But already the stench is high, especially around the canal to which scores had run in vain hope of safety."

The scene was in Tokyo, described by a special correspondent to the *Japan Chronicle* following a great earthquake on September 1, 1923. In a very short span of time the people of Tokyo and the vicinity were visited with perhaps the greatest single series of calamities in history. First there had been the earthquake, followed by huge tsunami, the great tidal waves that follow large earthquakes, and then fire, tornado, typhoon, landslide, flood and torrential rain had taken their toll. It was one of nature's most diversified and disastrous visitations upon the lives and homes of men.

The day had dawned with strong wind and a light rain, but the rain abated, the sky cleared, and the brilliant morning sun came out. Tokyo, Yokohama and other communities in the surrounding district began to swelter under the intense sun. Shortly before noon, the earthquake struck. It was lunchtime, and thousands of coal, charcoal and gas fires had been lit to prepare the midday meal. Wind picked up the flames and spread them, quickly engulfing large sections of Yokohama in billowing smoke. Swirling dust from collapsed buildings mingled with the smoke from hundreds of fires, turning the sky from yellow to brown to black.

Sampans in the bay caught fire and were driven by the rising gale. A seismic sea wave rose out of the bay and swept the shoreline, carrying flaming boats onto the land along with a terrifying cargo of floating bodies and burning debris.

While the fire was raging out of control, roiling gales from the typhoon coupled with intense heat from the fires stirred the atmosphere into

121

devastating violence. A tornado appeared in the late afternoon, scooping up huge masses of burning debris and spreading the fire over an ever-larger area.

In Honjo Ward, an estimated forty thousand persons had fled from falling and burning buildings. Smoke and fire quickly enveloped the scene and snatched away the ephemeral safety the refugees had sought. They and their belongings burst into flame. The place became a sea of fire as the tornado swept down on its victims. In all the history of great disasters, it was the closest to hell on earth. Only a handful of the forty thousand survived.

The fire continued to burn in Tokyo for three days, accompanied by frightening, relentless earth shocks. On the day of the earthquake there were 222 aftershocks, the next day 323, and then they came in slowly decreasing numbers.

Tokyo and Yokohama were almost totally destroyed, and an estimated number of citizens killed and missing was over 300,000.

Later the rains began, and the flooding, and what had not already slid during the major shocks began to slide. A hamlet containing some sixty families was buried under a layer of earth more than a hundred feet deep. A train bound for Manazuru with over two hundred passengers was carried away by floodwaters and sent to the bottom of Sagami Bay with every soul on board.

Although the aftereffects of the earthquake went on for several days, the initial destruction took place in the space of a few seconds, as another eyewitness attests. An American journalist, Henry W. Kinney, was in a train approaching Yokohama when the earthquake struck, and he describes what he saw:

"I glanced out just as the stone face of an embankment shot down over the tracks. It did not slide or tumble down: it literally shot down, as if compelled by a sudden, gigantic pressure from the top, the stones spreading in a twinkling over the right of way. A four-story concrete building vanished, disintegrated in the flash of an eye. Tiles cascaded with precipitate speed from the roofs. The one predominating idea that struck the mind was the almost incredible rapidity of the destruction."

The actual place in the earth where the quake originates is called the focus and the point on the surface immediately above is called the epicenter. In a large earthquake, the vibrations are felt over hundreds of thousands of square miles. This fact is well illustrated by the great Lisbon earthquake of November 1, 1755. The shock was felt over an area some 1,300,000 square miles. More than a third of Europe was aware of the quake. In Loch Lomond, over 1,000 miles from Lisbon, the waters oscillated as the earthquake waves raced through the earth.

At Amsterdam, also more than 1,000 miles away, water in the canals was agitated so violently that several boats broke loose from their moorings. In Sweden, 1,800 miles away from the epicenter, the River Dal overflowed.

About 15,000 people lost their lives in this tremendous eighteenth-century earthquake, and it almost completely destroyed the city of Lisbon. Three weeks after the quake, mounds of rubbish obliterated the streets and were still smoking. The Lisbon earthquake had a profound effect on eighteenth-century philosophy as thinkers tried to reconcile its destruction with their previous concepts of the gentleness of nature.

Samuel Chase was in Lisbon during the great quake, and described it and his own experiences in a letter to his sister in England:

"About three-quarters after nine o'clock in the morning, on Saturday, the 1st of November, 1755, I was alone in my bedchamber four stories from the ground, opening a bureau, when a shaking or trembling of the earth (which I knew immediately to be an earthquake), gentle at first, but gradually becoming violent, much alarmed me. Turning round to look at the window, the glass seemed to be falling out. Surprised at the continuation of the motion . . . I dreaded a catastrophe. . . ."

Chase rushed up a flight of stairs, to be confronted with a view of heaving houses so confusing that he wasn't sure what to do. He supported himself with an arm through a window and then, thinking the whole city was sinking into the earth, lost consciousness.

". . . Then, after I know not how long, just as if waking from a dream, with confused ideas, I found my mouth stuffed full of something that with my left hand I strove to get out; and not being able to breathe freely, struggled till my head was quite disengaged from the rubbish. In doing this I came to myself, and, recollecting what had happened, supposed the earthquake to be over; and from what I had so lately seen, expected to find the whole city fallen to the ground . . . I remained stupefied till the still falling tiles and rubbish made me seek for shelter. . . ."

Chase managed to squirm his way through the rubble until he finally emerged, and fell about two feet from the pile under which he had been buried into a small dark place from whence he emerged into a little room:

". . . where stood a Portuguese man covered with dust, who, the moment he saw me coming in that way, started back and, crossing himself all over, cried out, as their custom is when much surprised, 'Jesus, Mary and Joseph! Who are you? Where do you come from?' Of which being informed, he placed me in a chair. This done, clasping his hands together he lifted them and his eyes toward the ceiling, in show of the utmost distress and concern. This made me examine myself, which before I had not leisure to do. My right arm hung down before me motionless like a dead weight, the shoulder being out and the bone broken; my stockings were cut to pieces and my legs covered with wounds; the right ankle was swelled to prodigious size, with a fountain of blood spouting upward from it; that I could scarcely breathe; all the left side of my face likewise swelled up—the skin was beat off, and the blood streaming from it; with a great wound above, and a small one below the eye, and several bruises on my back and head. Barely had I perceived myself to be in this mangled condition when another shock, threatening as the first, came on."

The most severe American earthquake since the magnitude scale was invented occurred in Alaska on Good Friday, March 27, 1964, when an intensity of about 8.5 was reached: an energy release of some hundred sextillion ergs. With an epicenter near Prince William Sound in eastern Alaska, the earthquake affected an area of some 100,000 square miles, caused damage of 750 million dollars and killed 115 people.

The tectonic warping that was a notable feature of this earthquake affected an area of more than 50,000 square miles. In the northern half of the area, including Kenai Peninsula and Kodiak Island, the ground sank as much as eight feet. In the south, including most of Prince William Sound, it rose generally four to eight feet and in some places as much as 33 feet.

In Alaska's largest city, Anchorage, buildings and pavements dropped in places as much as 30 feet. The 470-mile long Alaska Railroad was so buckled and twisted that it was estimated it would cost 25 million dollars to repair it.

Offshore there were submarine slides and giant waves, known as tsunami. These waves inundated shorelines to nearly 40 feet, causing much loss of life and property along the southwest coastline of the Gulf of Alaska. Submarine landslides carried away the port facilities of Seward and Val-

126

dez. Some particularly violent surges of water left marks on the land up to 175 feet above low water.

Private First Class Clarence Myers, a cook at nearby Fort Richardson, was standing in the downtown shopping center of Anchorage when the earthquake hit. At first he assumed it was a small one, but as it continued without letup and then intensified he became terrified. Finally, he couldn't stay on his feet. He wanted to run, but looking wildly around him, he saw that there was nowhere to go.

The pavement was undulating all around him in waves, and cars were taking off and bouncing crazily against each other as the street buckled. People ran out of buildings, lurching to their knees as the agitated ground took away their balance. Parking meters and lamp posts toppled, and power lines began to give way, snapping to earth with crackles of live electricity. Falling, splintering glass was everywhere.

People running in the streets were for the most part oblivious to their own condition, although they were in every state of disarray. At one point a group of people clasped hands to form a chain in an attempt to protect against falling into huge cracks that were opening in the ground. A man ran from the steam room of the Athletic Club and joined them. He was stark naked. No one noticed or seemed to care.

While PFC Myers fought to regain his balance, he watched a horrible sight. A huge slab of concrete that had decorated the facade of the J. C.

Penney building slowly slid away. One section killed a man crouched on the sidewalk. Another crashed down on top of a station wagon, mashing it to a height of three feet. Myers could see there was a woman in the car, but there was nothing he could do to help her as long as the quake continued.

Inside the Penney building, two teen-agers who had been playing with the buttons in the self-service elevator were jammed between floors. They were later cut, unhurt, out of the elevator shaft with a blowtorch.

All over town, tall buildings suffered, swayed and cracked. On the 15th floor of the Anchorage-Westward Hotel Bob Reeve remembers being tossed from end to end of the room like a bouncing ball. In another building, a seventy-nine-year-old woman was alone in her tenth-floor apartment. Mrs. Alice Milligan had been talking to her daughter, Mary Louise Rasmussen, when the quake struck and the line went dead. She rode it out, with the building thrashing back and forth, everything out of the kitchen cupboards smashing on the floor. The wall mirror crashed to the floor and the windows fell out. Mrs. Milligan crawled under the living-room coffee table and prayed. After five horrifying minutes, the quaking stopped and it was over.

PFC Myers was one of the first to spring into action. He tried, with several other men, to move that concrete slab off the car he had watched being demolished. When the men couldn't move it, someone rounded up a wrecker and they were

128

finally able to prop the slab up on blocks. The woman still lay on the floor of the car. She was alive, but badly hurt. They cut her out of the car with a blowtorch, but she died the next morning.

Bob Reeve was joined by another man, Ken Yates, in inching his way down the fifteen floors of the building—which could collapse at any moment—between them and solid ground—which also no longer seemed quite so solid. A man at Mrs. Milligan's building appeared with a flashlight to help guide her down nine flights of stairs to the street. Mrs. Milligan looked up at the building once she was outside and saw giant cracks spidering up the walls. If she stayed near it, she knew she was risking the possibility it might collapse and bury her.

Mrs. Milligan set out to make her way to her daughter's home, and realized the enormity of what had happened in downtown Anchorage. The whole landscape was disorganized, in a shambles. Nothing of the familiar remained. One whole block on which she remembered shops and a theater, had been wiped out. The theater itself dropped ten feet below the sidewalk level, and the rest of the block stood stark and exposed, with upturned chunks of concrete poking out of rubble, marked here and there by giant fissures in the earth. Finally Mrs. Milligan found a taxi driver who agreed to take her to her daughter's home in Turnagain.

Meanwhile, at Turnagain, all was in chaos. A workman who had been working in the playroom had gone upstairs to talk to the maid when the tremor began. Suddenly, through the window, the workman, Balas Ervin, saw an incredible sight —the earth outside shot 50 feet into the air. Ervin and the maid didn't realize that a fissure had opened beneath the house and the house had plunged into the center of it.

Ervin grabbed the maid's hand and tried the front door but it was jammed. As they ran toward the back door, cans from the cupboards pelted against them and they were slammed violently from side to side. Outside they were unable to keep their balance on the lawn. They grabbed a sundial, but they were both shaken loose and tossed into the 50-foot deep crevasse.

Somehow, Ervin managed to boost the maid to the top of the fissure, and then scramble out himself. He could see then that the entire area was full of fissures, with houses in them. The Rasmuson house was in the middle of one of the worst cave-ins. Inside it were Mary Louise Rasmuson and her eighty-four-year-old grandmother, who had survived the quake as her bed rolled from side to side of the room all during the tremor.

A neighbor, Mr. Sholton, several teen-agers, and the workman, Ervin, all helped to rescue Mary Louise and the grandmother from their deep predicament, inching them up the icy cliff with ropes.

Although many were rescued, death stalked Anchorage that day with huge, shaking steps. Virgil and Lenora Wright were at home together when a bluff slid out from under them. Mrs. Knight never regained consciousness, and Mr. Knight lost a leg. Bill Taylor was killed when the 60-foot air traffic control tower at Anchorage International Airport collapsed. Twelve-year-old Perry Mead was killed along with the baby brother he was attempting to rescue. His father, a neurosurgeon, continued to operate on injured victims all through the night, although occasionally he had to pause, his eyes blinded with tears.

Elsewhere in Alaska, the damage was being compounded by the giant killer waves that stalked in the wake of the earthquake. On the island of Kodiak, resting in the Gulf of Alaska, most of the people led a quiet, primitive life. About 2,600 of the island's 7,500 population lived in its one city, Kodiak. The first hint of impending disaster at Kodiak was the quake itself, although the shock was far enough from the epicenter that not much damage was done.

In Shearwater Bay, however, the quake opened long fissures, and the bay itself rushed in. When the ground snapped shut, towering geysers shot toward the sky. At 5:36 P.M., rancher Ron Hurst heard the first hint of a low rumbling that preceded the sea wave heading toward the bay. He headed for high ground. Another rancher, Louis Beaty, was also on high ground. He had followed his cattle up there earlier in the afternoon, when they had instinctively left their low-lying grazing ground hours before their usual time. Residents of Kodiak City had been warned to evacuate to the mountains. The tsunami was rushing down the Gulf of Alaska with its 30-foot waves of death.

A tsunami is sometimes called a tidal wave, but it has no relation to tides, nor is it caused by underwater landslips. Seismologists generally agree that the great walls of water are the direct result of tectonic displacements under the ocean which are brought on by an earthquake.

Out in the harbor, Bill Cuthbert in his 86-foot crab boat *Selief* knew the tsunami was coming, but he couldn't leave. His engine didn't work, and there was no time to get to land and eventually make his way to high ground. He had to ride it out.

The first wave came at 6:47—a gradual swell, followed by a gradual ebb. Then the second wave hit, and in an instant, pilings, anchors, lines and piers gave way and the harbor became a whirlpool. Cuthbert and his two crewmen clung to the rail as the boat was tossed crazily about on the raging water. They tried to throw a line to a man in a small boat crying for help, but couldn't. They saw him carried off wildly in the swirling debris.

The third wave hit 55 minutes later, with less violence, but more height. Cuthbert's boat was whirled around and around and came to rest upright on the crushed remains of what had been a Kodiak store. The fourth wave, still less violent, refloated Cuthbert's scow, and he tied a line to a telephone pole. The waves continued throughout that long and terrible night, just about every 55 minutes, each one a little less violent than the last. Cuthbert ended up on the back of the Kodiak schoolhouse, five blocks from the shoreline.

There were other bizarre juxtapositions between the land and the sea that night in Kodiak. Kraft's store had been picked up on the first wave and carried out to sea, passing over the jetty at high water. On the next wave it was back again, and it continued to travel back and forth with the ebb and flow of the water, ending up only a few hundred yards from its original foundation, but unmistakably the worse for its unaccustomed voyaging.

Because of efficient warning, most of the people in small fishing villages on Kodiak Island escaped with their lives, but destruction to homes and property was almost complete. In one village, less fortunate than the others, 25 of the 72 villagers perished.

Elsewhere on Kodiak Island, Gordon L. Wallace had taken his family out for a picnic and sightseeing trip in Chiniak. He had his wife, Arlene, with him, and his son Jackie, seven. When the earthquake struck, they decided to try and make it back to the naval base where Wallace worked. They drove on until they reached a portion of the road so submerged they knew they could never cross it, and they decided to make a run for it. Wallace jumped out of the car and had just gotten a firm grip on the hands of his wife and son when the wave struck, knocking them all unconscious.

When Wallace came back to consciousness, he began calling for his family, but there was no response. He searched along the shoreline, shivering in the cold and stumbling from shock. When he found a fallen log, he began paddling out into the water among the debris, calling out again and again, but always there was no response.

He slept for a while on the shore, and then woke up and began his search again. He came to a fence and followed it for two miles to a farmhouse where he fainted again. The family at the farmhouse gave him emergency aid that saved his own life. In the morning, he set out again.

He returned to the road where the disaster had struck his family down, and from there he signaled a Navy tug for help and was taken back to the station. Once more he returned to the area, before sundown that day, but his search was hopelessly futile.

On Sunday, a search party found Arlene Wallace's body, covered with mud and debris, in the back seat of the demolished car. It had been swept half a mile inshore by the tsunami. A few feet from the car lay Jackie's body, covered with debris.

Earthquakes occur all over the world, but are especially abundant in well-defined tracts called seismic belts. One of these is the "Circle of Fire" which borders the Pacific Ocean on the north, east and west. Another stretches from the Mediterranean through the Alps, Caucasus and Himalayas to the East Indies. In these regions new mountain ranges are building, and in that building, earthquakes and volcanoes are the spectacular but superficial effects of vast underground activity.

134

The primary effects of earthquakes are those accomplished directly, by rock slippage, such as warping the earth's crust, forming cliffs, diverting waterfalls and rivers, offsetting highways, and crushing such structures as buildings and bridges. Secondary effects are those that result from the shaking, that is, from pressure waves sent out by the vibrations of the shock. Such effects include landslides, damming of streams, and collapse of distant buildings.

After an earthquake strikes, destruction can be quick and complete. Railroad tracks are bent and shifted out of line. Bridges are weakened. Tunnels collapse. Irrigation is disrupted, in part by power lines being downed and pumping curtailed. Dams are broken and their waters sent cascading downstream. Submarine cables can be cut directly, or indirectly, by the earthquake.

Despite the tremendous hazard to life in the earthquake zones, a good part of those areas is thickly inhabited. In some areas, nothing less than a mass evacuation could ensure immunity from disastrous quakes which periodically devastate the country, and in places like Japan and California such mass evacuation is clearly impracticable. In such regions, architects and seismologists can do much to reduce the danger, and much is now known about the kind of building which will be most resistant to earthquake damage. No building is completely proof against earthquakes, however. And no one living in a known earthquake zone can hope to escape the experience of having the earth beneath his feet turn into a quaking, terrifyingly unstable platform as the crust of the earth shifts and realigns itself in new patterns.

CHAPTER EIGHT

Volcano

"We had been watching the volcano sending up smoke. The Captain said to my mistress, 'I am not going to stay any longer than I can help.' I went to the cabin and was assisting with the dressing of the children when the steward rushed past and shouted, 'Close the cabin door—the volcano is coming!' We closed the door and at the same moment came a terrible explosion which nearly burst the eardrums. The vessel was lifted high into the air, and then seemed to be sinking down. We were all thrown off our feet by the shock and huddled crouching in the corner of the cabin. My mistress had the baby girl in her arms,

137

the older girl leaned on my left arm, while I held little Eric in my right.

"The explosion seemed to have blown in the skylight over our heads, and before we could raise ourselves, hot moist ashes began to pour in on us; they came in boiling splattering splashes like hot mud, without any pieces of rock. In vain we tried to shield ourselves. The cabin was pitch dark . . . we could see nothing. . . .

"A sense of suffocation came next. When the door burst open, air rushed in and we revived somewhat. When we could see each other's faces, they were all covered with black lava. The baby was dying; Rita, the older girl, was in great agony and every part of my body was paining me. A heap of hot mud had collected near us and as Rita put her hand down to raise herself up it was plunged up to the elbow in the scalding stuff. . . .

"The first engineer came now, and hearing our moans carried us to the forward deck and there we remained on the burning ship from 8:30 A.M. until 3:00 P.M. The crew was crowded forward, many in a dying condition. The whole ship was one mass of roaring flames and the saloon aft as well as the forward part of the ship were burning fiercely, but afterwards they put out the fire.

"My mistress lay on the deck in a collapsed state; the little boy was already dead, and the baby dying. The lady was collected and resigned, handed me some money, told me to take Rita to her aunt, and sucked a piece of ice before she died."

This is the story of a Barbados nursemaid who,

with one of her charges, was one of the very few survivors of the eruption of Mt. Pelée on May 8, 1902. St. Pierre was a prosperous town on the northwest coast of Martinique in the Caribbean. About five miles away, Mont Pelée had been quiet for about 50 years, but previous eruptions of the volcano had covered the countryside with rich volcanic ash, and the land was planted in valuable sugar cane.

In April, 1902, Pelée began to awaken. There were some earthquake shocks and mild eruptions which dusted the streets. The activity slowly increased, and by the end of the month, noxious ash was raining down on the town. By the first week of May, the rain of ashes was continuous. Everything was covered with ashes. Puffs of wind blew clouds of stifling dust from roofs and awnings into the eyes of the people. Birds fell from the sky. Horses refused to work. Cattle were asphyxiated.

The wife of the American Consul described the situation in a letter: "The smell of sulphur is so strong, that horses on the street stop and snort, and some of them drop in their harness and die from suffocation. Many of the people are obliged to wear wet handkerchiefs to protect them from the strong fumes of sulphur."

On May 5, a cataract of boiling mud coursed down the mountain at express-train speed, engulfing a sugar mill and killing 30 workmen.

People began to panic in St. Pierre. Some left, more got ready to leave. Frightful detonations were shaking the island, and Pelée was discharg-

139

ing an enormous column of dense black smoke, saturated with ashes and cinders. Forests on the outskirts of town and on the slopes of the mountain were burning.

During the night of May 7, Pelée gave its final warning. Monsieur Parel, the vicar-general of Martinique, recorded his impressions of the incredible display:

"Since four o'clock in the morning, when I was awakened in my room by loud detonations, I have been watching the most extraordinary pyrotechnic display: at one moment a fiery crescent gliding over the surface of the crater, at the next long, perpendicular gashes of flame piercing the column of smoke, and then a fringe of fire, encircling the dense clouds rolling above the furnace of the crater. Two glowing craters from which fire issued, as if from blast furnaces, were visible during half an hour, the one on the right a little above the other.

"I distinguished clearly four kinds of noises; first, the claps of thunder, which followed the lightning at intervals of twenty seconds; then the mighty muffled detonations of the volcano, like the roaring of many cannon fired simultaneously; third, the continuous rumbling of the crater, which the inhabitants designated the 'roaring of the lion'; and then last, as though furnishing the bass for this gloomy music, the deep noise of the swelling waters, of all the torrents which take their source upon the mountain, generated by an overflow such as had never yet been seen. This immense rising of thirty streams at

140

once, without one drop of water having fallen on the seacoast, gives some idea of the cataracts which must pour down upon the summit from the storm clouds gathered around the crater."

The next morning dawned bright and sunny, and the only sign of activity on Mont Pelée was a huge vapor column rising high into the air. Awake early, Fernand Clerc, one of Martinique's leading planters, noticed his barometer needle agitating wildly. He took alarm and piled his family into a carriage, driving out of the city shortly after 7 A.M. He reached Mont Parnasse, a mile from St. Pierre, stopped the carriage, got out and looked back. It was 7:50 A.M.—zero hour— and Pelée would wait and warn no longer.

As Clerc watched, an eruption burst from the main crater on Pelée, and at the same instant the volcano's side opened with a roaring explosion. A vast black cloud shot out horizontally at enormous speed. It was as if the other three sides of Pelée formed the mouth of a tremendous cannon from which shot a bolt of superheated vapor, gas and white-hot fragments of molten rock.

This tremendous blast rushed down the slopes of Pelée like a hurricane of black fog. There was a continuous roar of staccato explosions like a gun battery in action. Continuous lightning played about the descending cloud. Rapidly expanding gases were constantly exploding.

Clerc, watching from the safety of Mont Parnasse, said the blast covered the five miles to St. Pierre in two or three minutes. Two other observers, one watching from Mont Parnasse and one from the deck of a vessel in the harbor, said the blast swept across St. Pierre itself in two or three *seconds*. It then fanned out to sea.

St. Pierre was hit by a hurricane-force barrage of red-hot sand and stones. It was set ablaze from end to end almost instantaneously. The crew of the ship *Pouyer-Quertier*, lying about six miles out to sea, saw two giant flashes from Pelée, then light in the direction of St. Pierre. Thirty seconds later, through the binoculars, they saw that the town was in flames.

With the exception of one man who miraculously escaped, most of St. Pierre's 30,000 inhabitants were wiped out before they knew what hit them. One breath of that fiery cloud and a man's lungs shriveled away. But some bodies were found in positions indicating that an attempt had been made to flee. Captain Freeman, on the *Roddam* in the harbor, heard above the roaring of the volcano the terrifying cries of agony and despair from the thousands who were perishing in St. Pierre. Against the flames of the city he saw a few people running wildly about the beach, but it was only a temporary view, for the fire and overwhelming cloud caught them in their tracks and he saw no more.

One of the most vivid accounts of the destruction of St. Pierre is that of Assistant Purser Thompson, who was in the harbor on board the *Roraima* when the volcano erupted:

"I saw St. Pierre destroyed. The city was blotted out by one great flash of fire. Nearly

40,000 people were killed at once. Of eighteen vessels lying in the roads, only one, the British steamship *Roddam* escaped and she, I hear, lost half of those on board. It was a dying crew that took her out. Our boat, the *Roraima,* arrived at St. Pierre early Thursday morning. For hours before entering the roadstead we could see flames and smoke rising from Mt. Pelée. No one on board had any idea of danger. Captain G. T. Muggah was on the bridge, and all hands got on deck to see the show. The spectacle was magnificent. As we approached St. Pierre we could distinguish the rolling and leaping of red flames that belched from the mountain in huge volumes and gushed into the sky. Enormous clouds of black smoke hung over the volcano. . . . There was a constant muffled roar. It was like the bigest oil refinery in the world burning up on the mountain top. There was a tremendous explosion about 7:45, soon after we got in. The mountain was blown to pieces. There was no warning. The side of the volcano was ripped out and there was hurled straight toward us a solid wall of flame. It sounded like a thousand cannon.

"The wave of fire was on us and over us like a flash of lightning. It was like a hurricane of fire. I saw it strike the cable steamship *Grappler* broadside on, and capsize her. From end to end she burst into flames and then sank. The fire rolled in mass straight down upon St. Pierre and the shipping. The town vanished before our eyes.

"The air grew stifling hot and we were in the

thick of it. Wherever the mass of fire struck the sea, the water boiled and sent up vast columns of steam. The sea was torn into huge whirlpools that careened toward the open sea. One of these horrible, hot whirlpools swung under the *Roraima* and pulled her down on her beam end with the suction. She careened way over to port, and then the fire hurricane from the volcano smashed her, and over she went on the opposite side. The fire wave swept off the masts and smokestacks as if they were cut by a knife.

"Captain Muggah was the only one on the deck not killed outright. He was caught by the fire wave and was terribly burned. He yelled to get up the anchor, but before two fathoms were heaved in, the *Roraima* was almost upset by the boiling whirlpool and the fire wave had thrown her down on her beam ends to starboard. Captain Muggah was overcome by the flames. He fell unconscious from the bridge and overboard. The blast of fire from the volcano lasted only a few minutes. It shrivelled and set fire to everything it touched. Thousands of casks of rum were stored in St. Pierre, and these were exploded by the terrific heat. The burning rum ran in streams down every street and out into the sea. This blazing rum set fire to the *Roraima* several times.

"Before the volcano burst, the landings of St. Pierre were covered with people. After the explosion, not one living soul was seen on the land. Only twenty-five of those on board were left after the first blast. . . . It looked as if the entire north end of the island was on fire."

Although the glowing cloud, called *nuée ardente,* which descended from Pelée was composed of hot gases and incandescent particles, within the cloud there was almost no free oxygen, and thus no actual combustion. It was only after the cloud had passed that the city took flame, with the inrushing oxygen that followed the cloud's passage.

During those few seconds that the *nuée ardente* was passing over the town, the heat was so intense that many objects were carbonized, or turned to charcoal without combustion. Some wooden beams four inches thick were instantly charred by the intense heat. Books with charcoal pages were found after the disaster, and food was found in a petrified state. In the heart of the city, iron bars were found twisted like pretzels. Alongside the charred body of a man was a box of matches which had not been ignited, probably due to lack of oxygen.

In all that unbelievable holocaust, there were some who remained alive. One of them was Leon Compere-Leandre, a Negro shoemaker whose home was on the outskirts of the area affected by the glowing cloud. He felt his arms, legs, and body burning and could hardly move. Several other people sought refuge in his house, crying and writhing in pain, and he saw one young girl fall dead after about ten seconds. In another room he found his father, still clothed, lying on a bed, dead. His body was purple and inflated, but the clothing was intact. In his courtyard were two interlocked corpses. All about him were dead bodies, and after only a few minutes he heard no more human cries. Leandre managed to make his way out of the flaming city. There is no adequate explanation for why he survivied.

Another survivor was August Ciparis, who weathered the holocaust in a jail cell. He never knew at the time what was happening. He only knew the writhing agony of searing heat and near suffocation. His clothing did not catch fire, but he was severely burned over almost all his body. He lay in his cell for four days before he was rescued.

Death came to the citizens of St. Pierre in three main ways: from the effects of the hurricanelike blast of the cloud, resulting in the collapse of buildings; from scorching and asphyxiation by the hot and poisonous gases; and from fires after the cloud had passed. It has not yet been adequately explained how those two men, of all the 30,000 people in St. Pierre, should have escaped with their lives.

Immediately following the blast, the dust it liberated and the vapor column which was simultaneously ejected out of the main crater threw a dense pall over St. Pierre and the surrounding countryside. On Mont Parnasse, where Clerc was still observing, it was so dark that the man couldn't see his own children an arm's length away. Men on the two surviving ships in the harbor could not see across the deck. The total darkness lasted for half an hour.

Then a new horror began, that was so vividly

described by the nursemaid who survived and watched her mistress die. Torrential rain swept thousands of tons of volcanic ash down Pelée's slopes, and a deluge of soft pasty mud cascaded into St. Pierre, burying many houses to their rooftops. The mud was steaming hot and of the consistency of thin cement, and wherever it fell it formed a coating which later hardened like cement.

The shock waves of the great blast raced around the earth, and the noise was heard at least 300 miles away. There was even a report from Maracaibo, 800 miles from Martinique, of a sound as if immense explosions were being fired high in the air.

The rescue ship *Marin* from Fort de France arrived at St. Pierre three and a half hours after the disaster, but the heat from the burning town was so great that she could not approach the shore. The fire was so furious that neither the torrential rain nor the avalanche of mud had been able to put it out.

When rescue parties eventually made their way into St. Pierre, they found that the devastation was total and appalling. The pretty yellow-and-white town of St. Pierre was a heap of dirty, blackened rubble. Three-foot-thick walls of stone and cement had been torn to pieces by the volcanic whirlwind. A statue of the Virgin Mary, weighing three tons, had been flung some 50 feet from its pedestal. It has been estimated that a wind speed of around 300 mph was required to have accomplished this.

The temperature of the blast was not less than 450 degrees C., and some of the particles of molten rock which were swept along by it may have had an internal temperature of over 1,000 degrees C.

The condition of some of the corpses gave a vivid impression of the swiftness with which death had overtaken most of St. Pierre's population. There was a clerk bent over a ledger, frozen in rigor mortis with a pen still in his hand. A man was bent, dead, over a washbasin from which the water had evaporated. In one house, an entire family sat around a table. Some had apparently staggered a few steps before they died, as they lay with contorted bodies, hands clutching at scalded mouths and throats. One of the passengers on a ship in the harbor was missing his tongue, it had literally been burned out of his head.

Many bodies were found naked. Many others had burst abdomens and split skulls. Such wounds indicate that the sudden reduction in the surrounding air pressure caused the bodies to explode. Those who survived on the *Roraima* in the harbor said it was impossible to breathe while the blast lasted, as the air was too hot, and that after the blast the air seemed like a vacuum, and it was almost impossible to get any oxygen into the lungs.

A young traveler, A. L. Koster, who took some of the first photographs of the dead city of St. Pierre, went in while the ground was still too hot to walk on comfortably, and his description of the scene is compelling:

"Evidence of terrific heat was everywhere. The

bodies of victims strewn among the ruins were greatly reduced in size. It was as if most of the moisture had suddenly been extracted from them. But as they were not burned, and as trees and other pieces of wood were barely charred, I concluded that either the duration of the heat had been extremely brief or that the heat had failed to ignite anything because of an absence of oxygen."

A few days after the initial eruption, another cloud exploded and roared along the same path, toppling the few remaining walls in St. Pierre. There were new paroxysmal eruptions on May 26, June 6, July 9 and August 30. For months Pelée continued to belch forth incandescent, superheated steam clouds. Then, in October, from Pellée's crater a vast mass of solidified lava slowly rose until it formed a gigantic rock obelisk. Eventually, the tower of lava reached 1,000 feet above the crater, with a diameter at its base of between 350 and 500 feet. It gradually disintegrated, and disappeared toward the end of 1904.

Angelo Heilprin, who had climbed almost to Pelée's summit after the 1902 blast, visited Martinique a year later and describes the towering lava shaft with awe:

"The spectacle was one of overwhelming grandeur, and we stood for some moments awed and silent in the shadow of this most impressive of mountain forms. Nature's monument dedicated to the 30,000 dead who lay in the silent city below, it rose up a huge monolith . . . a unique and incomparable type in our planet's wonderland.

. . . In its condition of vapor clouds blowing out from its base and from the cone that supported it, with blue sulphur smoke curling its way along these, it presented a spectacle of almost overwhelming grandeur and one of terrorizing effect which could hardly be matched elsewhere. None of the grand scenes of nature which I had before seen . . . impressed me to the extent that did the view of Pelée's tower. . . ."

Both active and dormant volcanoes are found widely scattered over the surface of the earth. There may be as many as five hundred active vents, and many thousands more which are dormant or extinct. They are distributed in a fairly orderly manner, and generally follow areas of major crustal weakness and stress. They are connected with geologically youthful mountains and the unimaginable subterranean stresses and processes which produce them, and are of relatively minor significance in terms of the tectonic forces at work beneath the earth's crust.

Each volcano is an individual, but there are two features which every volcano shares in common. First, at some stage in its history, every volcano has an open vent connecting a subterranean reservoir of magma, or molten rock, with the surface of the earth. Second, the materials ejected through this conduit accumulate around the external opening, and form the characteristic volcanic cone as they cool and harden.

There are three stages in the life of every volcano, active, dormant and extinct. An active volcano is one which has had a period of eruptive activity during recorded history, when solid, liquid or gaseous products were liberated from the internal magma chamber. A dormant volcano is one which in the period of recorded history has remained in a comatose state. Dormant volcanoes have probably been active in the recent geologic past, and are still potentially active, but the next eruptive phase of a dormant volcano cannot be easily determined. An extinct volcano is one which, of course, has ceased activity.

These categories are rather indistinct, since they depend to a certain extent on the likelihood of written records having been made, and there is considerable overlapping between the active and dormant categories. Also, it is difficult to determine when a volcano has passed from dormancy to extinction. Thus most volcanoes are difficult to classify.

Active volcanoes are generally recognized as being of one of five basic eruption types: Icelandic, Hawaiian, Strombolian, Vulcanian and Peléan.

Icelandic eruptions are characterized by the mass discharge of great floods of molten basaltic lavas from deep-rooted fissures in the earth's crust. A primary feature of the mass-fissure eruption is the lack of a central or well-defined volcanic edifice. The bulk of Iceland was formed in this manner, as was the Columbia Plateau in the northwestern United States.

Hawaiian eruptions have formed the bulk of the Hawaiian islands. Two of the volcanoes there,

Mauna Loa and Kilauea, are often eruptive. In this kind of eruption, basic basaltic lavas in a fluid state are extruded regularly with very little explosive activity.

Strombolian eruptions are more explosive than Hawaiian eruptions. The prototype is Stromboli, located in the Aeolian Islands north of Sicily, a volcano which has been in a state of continuous periodic eruptivity since the beginning of recorded history. In Stromboli's eruptions, the basaltic flow is less fluid than Hawaiian lava, and the molten material congeals in the vent, forming a thin, crusted surface between the closely spaced eruptions. When the explosion occurs, incandescent lava and crusty clots are hurled through the air, many of them falling back into the crater. The mild explosions are accompanied by emissions of steam and other gases.

Vulcanian, or Vesuvian eruptions began with a resting phase, after the crater-clearing explosions of the previous cycle. The first phase of new activity is the emission of gases, which is followed by the formation of small cinder cones on the crater floor. Then basaltic lava is emitted sporadically until the crater is gradually filled. When this is accomplished, the volcano is ready for its culminating blast. The pressure beneath the plugged crater results in powerful explosions which break up and eject the obstruction from the crater along with magma from the chamber below. The violent explosions associated with this type of eruption sometimes disrupt the structure of the mountain, and breaches may develop in

152

the crater or on the flanks of the cone. Lava may issue from these fissures, as well as from the explosive mouth of the cone.

Peléan eruptions are the most violent and potentially the most deadly. The magmas involved are extremely viscous. No liquid extrusions of lava take place. Instead, the vent of the volcano becomes plugged by a slowly rising column of stiff, semisolid magma which solidifies in the conduit, producing a seal of rock. The rising magma becomes supersaturated with withheld gases, and the molten material builds to a pressure head beneath the blocked vent.

In this variety of eruption, an emulsion cloud of superheated gases, dust, ash and larger incandescent particles is formed and due to its high density follows downhill slopes rather than rising. The cloud travels at speeds of more than one hundred miles per hour, leveling everything in its path.

Erupting volcanoes are not a unilaterally destructive phenomenon. They have provided scientists with firsthand evidence of the composition of the earth. Valuable chemical products are obtained from volcanic substances. Volcanic ash helps replace topsoil lost by erosion, and some of the world's most beautiful and fertile areas, such as the Caribbean chain of islands and the Hawaiian area, have been built by volcanic action.

The immense energies stored in volcanoes could, if harnessed, provide a virtually inexhaustible source of power. Iceland, New Zealand and California have all made practical use of volcanic steam, and the first power plant in the United States to be operated by natural steam was opened in 1960 in Sonoma County, California.

Many more people have been killed by earthquakes than by volcanoes, but for the town of St. Pierre, Pelée proved to be an evil demon indeed.

CHAPTER NINE

Tidal Wave

". . . We were sleeping peacefully when we were awakened by a loud hissing sound, which sounded for all the world as if dozens of locomotives were blowing off steam directly outside our house. Puzzled, we jumped up and rushed to the front window. Where there had been a beach previously, we saw nothing but boiling water, which was sweeping over the ten-foot top of the beach ridge and coming directly at the house. I rushed and grabbed my camera . . . by that time I was conscious of the fact that we might be experiencing a tsunami. My suspicions became confirmed as the water moved swiftly seaward, and the sea level dropped a score of feet, leaving the coral reefs in front of the house exposed to view . . . in a few minutes as I stood at the edge of the beach ridge in front of the house, I could see the water beginning to rise and swell up around the outer edges of the exposed reef. It built higher and higher and then came racing forward with amazing velocity."

Francis Shepard called to his wife, who had already started to run to the back of their house for protection and arrived in the somewhat sheltered spot himself just in time to look back and see water flooding the spot where he had stood only moments before. Then:

"Suddenly we heard the terrible smashing of glass at the front of the house. The refrigerator passed us on the left side moving upright out into the cane field. On the right came a wall of water sweeping toward us down the road that was our escape route from the area. . . . Finally the water stopped coming on and we were left on a small island . . . we started running along the emerging beach in the only direction in which we could get to the slightly elevated main road."

With nearby houses reduced to shambles on either hand, the Shepards rushed frantically through the fields as another wave began to move in over the reef. The incredible wall of water swept after them, flattening fields and chasing them with a frightening noise that hurried their running feet. Shepard's account goes on:

"Finally, after about six waves had moved on,

each one apparently getting progressively weaker, I decided I had better go back and see what I could rescue from what was left of the house where we had been living. After all, we were in scanty attire and required clothes. I had just reached the door when I became conscious that a very powerful mass of water was bearing down on the place. This time there simply was no island in back of the house during the height of the wave. I rushed to a nearby tree and climbed it as fast as possible and then hung on for dear life as I swayed back and forth under the impact of the wave. Like the others, this wave soon subsided, and the series of waves that followed were all minor in comparison."

This account, by Francis P. Shepard in *The Earth Beneath the Sea,* describes a gigantic seismic sea wave that struck Hawaii on April 1, 1946. At 2:00 A.M. that morning, a violent subterranean earth shock jolted the ocean floor of the Aleutian Trench, seventy miles southeast of Alaska's Unimak Island. Not long after the shock, a series of waves more than a hundred miles long began to spread outward, heading south at speeds up to six hundred miles an hour.

At six o'clock, gray storm clouds scudded across the Pacific off Kilauea Point, in the Hawaiian Islands. At Haena Bay, some women were cooking breakfast. Most of Honolulu was still asleep. Along the edge of Hilo Bay, palm trees were bending in the wind.

At six-nineteen, the first assault wave struck the northern coast of Kauai. At the head of

Haena Bay, two women, one of them carrying a baby, were caught by the swiftly rising water as they stood in front of their houses. They swam to safety, clinging desperately to nearby trees as they watched their houses being broken up and floated away. The power of the water was such that beach sand was dumped four feet deep across a highway in one place. Blocks of coral from offshore reefs were carried five hundred feet inland, and ten-ton blocks of limestone were tossed up on the reef itself.

In less than an hour the wave swept around all eight of the islands, bringing disaster with its swirling waters. And throughout the day, disaster mounted as wave after wave roared into the helpless islands. It was the worst seismic sea wave in the history of Hawaii. The seismic sea wave, also properly termed a tsunami, is often known by the misnomer "tidal wave," although the gigantic waves which periodically wreak havoc around the margins of the Pacific Ocean have nothing to do with tides. The name tidal wave probably derives from the appearance along an open coast where there are no reefs, of a rapidly rising tide.

In the Hawaiian Islands, the series of tsunamis that swept in in 1946, brought terrible destruction. Houses were demolished, victims were washed into bays. At Hilo, the destruction was particularly bad. Wave force at the mouth of the Wailuku River ripped out the railroad bridge there and carried one of its steel spans 750 feet upstream. Most of the buildings along Kamehameha Avenue were either destroyed, damaged or shifted, leaving the street in complete wreckage.

Fortunately, the heaviest concentration of population on the islands lay protected from the direct frontal assault on the south side of Oahu, but still there were 159 dead at the end of the day and 163 hospitalized. All over the islands, property was damaged, sometimes freakishly. Railroad tracks had been wrapped around trees. Eighty-eight tons of sugar had dissolved from the Hilo docks in the inundating water. Bridges and piers were collapsed, trees uprooted, and gardens destroyed. One house at Kawela Bay on Oahu, was gently lifted and carried two hundred feet inland, and then set down in a cane field with breakfast still cooking on the stove. Near Almaloa Gulch, waves carried one house along a shore ridge, dumped it, picked up another on the return and deposited it at the brink of high tide.

Most tsunamis have their origin in the great sea trenches that surround the margin of the Pacific Ocean. Six prominent locations produce the majority of Pacific Ocean tsunamis, lying off the coasts of the Aleutians, Japan, Chile, Kamchatka, Mexico and the Solomon Islands. There are no deep trenches along the west coast of the United States, which is probably why no appreciable tsunami have been observed along the California coast. Almost all tsunamis are preceded by tremendous earthquakes. Waves are most likely caused by faulting, a sudden dropping or lifting of a segment of the ocean bottom, which displaces large amounts of water. Another explanation is that huge submarine landslides produce the waves. Tsunamis are most generally the result of large earthquakes, although they are also, less frequently, caused by volcanic eruptions.

The tsunami that hit Hawaii in 1946 did damage elsewhere as well. The waves reached 115 feet up the rocky shore of Unimak Island in the Aleutians. Smaller waves from this earthquake were recorded all the way from Yakutat Bay, Alaska to Valparaiso, Chile.

Tsunamis move at an enormous speed in the open ocean, averaging about 450 miles an hour. Speed varies with the depth of the water, but always a terrific force is built up behind the wave, propelling it far inland and contributing to its potential for damage.

One of the most destructive waves of all time was caused not by an earthquake, but by the eruption of Krakatoa, a volcanic island between Sumatra and Java, in 1883. The explosion of Krakatoa sent eighteen cubic miles of debris into the air, creating hundred-foot waves which killed more than thirty-six thousand persons and obliterated more than a thousand villages. A remarkable account of that great wave has been written by Louis V. Housel, who was on board a sloop in the harbor of Frederickstadt, Santa Cruz, when the wave struck:

"Nothing unusual attracted our attention until three o'clock in the afternoon of the 18th of

November, when our vessel began to quiver and rock as if a mighty giant hand laid hold of her and was trying to loosen every timber in her frame. Officers and men ran pell-mell on deck to ascertain the cause of such a phenomenon. The vibrations continued the space of perhaps a minute, accompanied by a buzzing noise somewhat like the draught of a smelting-furnace or the hum of innumerable swarms of bees.

". . . I looked toward Frederickstadt and saw a dusty, hazy atmosphere over the town. I could see men, women and children running hither and thither and could catch faint cries of distress.

". . . An effort was made to man the starboard compressor so as to check the other anchor when let go; but the men had come on deck and were standing panic-stricken, gazing at the terrible appearance of the sea. A reef had risen off the northern point of the island where, but a few minutes before were several fathoms of water. Our vessel advanced toward and receded from the shore with the waters until, as if some great power had raised up the bottom of the bay, the sea rapidly closed in on the town, filling the houses and covering the street running along the beach to the depth of twenty-four feet. Our ship, following the current, took a course toward the southern end of the town, until, over the edge of the street, it swung her bow toward the north and was carried along, smashing a frame store-house and breaking down a row of shade trees.

". . . By this time the rush of waters was toward the ocean. We were carried out perhaps five hundred yards from the shore, when our vessel grounded, and the water continuing its retreat, she careened over on her port beam's ends. The bottom of the roadstead was now visible, nearly bare, for a distance of about half a mile beyond us, and that immense body of water which had covered the bay and part of the town was reforming, with the whole Atlantic Ocean as an ally, for a tremendous charge upon us and the shore. This was the supreme moment of the catastrophe. As far as the eye could reach to the north and to the south was a high, threatening wall of green water. It seemed to pause for a moment, as if marshaling its strength, and then on it came in a majestic, unbroken column, more awe-inspiring than an army with banners. The suspense was terrible. Our noble vessel seemed as a tiny nutshell to withstand the shock of the mighty, rushing Niagara that was advancing upon us. Many a hasty prayer was muttered by lips unaccustomed to devotion. All expected to be engulfed, and but few had any hope of surviving."

The first blow of the water sent the ship over on her starboard beam ends, and by the time she righted herself the water was well under her and she was carried broadside to the shore, landing again at the edge of a street where she rested.

The waves that followed the eruption of Krakatoa showed on tide gauges all the way around the world, even in the English Channel.

In July, 1958, one of the largest seismic sea waves ever recorded took place in Lituya Bay along the south coast of Alaska. The location is uninhabited, but three fishing boats were located at the lower end of the bay. A great earthquake occurred as a result of movement along a fault at the head of the bay, six miles from the location of the boats. The earthquake shook 40 million cubic yards of rock, weighing 90 million tons and falling from a maximum height of about 3,000 feet into Gilbert Inlet at the head of the bay. The tremendous rockfall sent a vast wave racing across the bay at about 100 mph. The boatment saw the commotion, and in a few minutes saw the great wave coming toward them down the bay.

One boat was lifted completely over the spit at the entrance of the bay by the front of the wave, and the occupants were so high they could look down on the eight-foot fir trees growing on the spit. They were dropped and the boat sank, but they escaped in a skiff. Another boat was at anchor, but the wave parted the anchor cable; but it had held long enough to prevent them from being carried over the spit. The third boat simply disappeared.

The wave had swept along the side of the bay at about the 100-foot level, but across a narrow inlet on the wall opposite the largest fall of rocks, the water had surged to a maximum height of 1,740 feet—a third of a mile, nearly twice the height of the Eiffel Tower. Four square miles of forest were destroyed. Trees with diameters as large as four feet were either washed out or snapped off at ground level. The spit is today denuded of life, a grim reminder of the greatest wave in the recorded history of man.

The earthquake that devasted Chile in May 1960 generated tsunamis that had far-reaching consequences. The day after the first report of the earthquake hit the news wires, the initial tsunami casualties were made known. A small village on the Chilean coast near Ancud was struck by a sweep of water that took 130 lives. In Lemu, another Chilean costal town, a huge wave swept in on helpless villagers. Very quickly then, the tsunami began to spread. At Juneau, Alaska, a fifteen-foot wave swept Montague Island near Cordova. Surges were reported in two widely separated points in British Columbia. Giant waves pounded the eastern coast of the Philippines. Dozens of small craft were torn loose from their moorings in the harbor at Sydney, Australia, by another wave. At Pitcairn Island, in mid-Pacific, there were reports of a forty-foot wave.

In Hawaii, there were radio warnings issued; nevertheless many were killed. At Hilo, the first wave was only about three feet high, but three subsequent waves, each one much larger destroyed huge sections of the city. The scene was one of devastation. One building was sucked completely across a street. Houses were carried blocks inland, many injuries were reported, and the cries of people trapped in buildings echoed pathetically.

In Japan, many islands had no warning of

the rushing tsunami. On Tuesday, May 24, the waves came in and raked Japan from Hokkaido in the north to the small Amami group of islands in the south. Thirty-three were reported dead by noon of that day and ninety-eight people were missing. Forty-one hundred homes were destroyed and thousands of others were severely damaged. Telephone lines were down, and early reports did not include all casualties.

Both Hawaii and Japan suffered major disasters as a result of the waves generated by the Chilean earthquake. When the water subsided in Japan, 150,000 people were left homeless. Twenty-five villages and towns had been hit. Ten of them had been completely submerged. In Hilo, some of the people originally reported missing were never found. Apparently they had been carried out to sea in the vast, swirling, choking surge of water that did sixty million dollars' worth of damage to the city of Hilo.

One of the greatest killer waves of all time occurred on June 15, 1896 and devasted Japan. In Sanriku, on the island of Honshu, many of the villagers were on the beaches when, at 7:30 in the evening, the earth trembled beneath their feet. The earthquake itself was relatively mild and did little damage, since the epicenter was fairly far away, on the slopes of the Tuscarora Deep.

About twenty minutes after the mild shock, the sea level began to fall. More and more of the coastal shore became visible as the water receded beyond the usual low tide mark and kept going.

Out and out it went, farther and farther, exposing parts of the sea floor never before seen. No one was alarmed. Many people walked out onto the exposed sand, wondering at the fish flapping, stranded. Then, from far out to sea, there was a faint murmur, like the sound of rain.

The noise continued to grow louder and louder until it became a roar like thunder. People began to panic and run back toward land, but it was too late. Much too late. With terrifying speed, the water began to return, rising higher and higher until it became a solid, seething wall of water, towering in some places to 100 feet. With a tremendous roar that drowned out the terrified cries of people who had begun to run too late, the wall of water swept over the beaches, the harbors, the villages, the fields, and far up into inlets and streams that flowed toward the shore.

In only a few minutes, twenty-eight thousand people were drowned. In some villages, such as Kamaishi, the losses were so great that there was almost nothing left. In Kamaishi, 72 percent of the people were drowned.

The effects of that great tsunami were felt on the farther shores of the Pacific, at California, 5,000 miles away, and it was two days before disturbances died away.

CONCLUSION

"Everybody talks about the weather, but nobody does anything about it." This remark, often attributed to Mark Twain, was uttered by a man named Charles Dudley Warren, in disgust, when people were still talking about the Blizzard of '88 at the end of the warm summer that followed it. The remark is so apt that it remains a classic comment on the fact of natural disaster.

Hurricanes produce more widespread destruction than any other atmospheric disturbance, yet all the modern scientific techniques available today have yielded no defense against them. The best man can do in the face of a hurricane is hide or run away, neither of which responses necessarily precludes personal disaster. Increasing study of hurricanes will yield knowledge of their complex structure, but the main value of such knowledge will be more accurate forecasting and earlier warning to those in the storm's path.

Flood control is in some ways fairly effective. The preventive measures which can contain flooding include levees and dykes, reservoirs and dams, mechanical enlargement of existing river channels diversion of floodwaters into secondary channels and the improved use of farm lands to increase the absorptive power of the land in a river basin. However, there is a limit to how far man can go in building defenses against invading water. After centuries of battle, Holland's formidable defenses were not able to withstand the combination of meteorological circumstances that caused the North Sea to rip them away, and there are many other examples of even the most elaborate systems being wiped out by unusual flooding.

Even today we do not completely understand the weather factors that produce tornadoes, and forecasting the approach of such storms is sometimes impossible. Even when the Weather Bureau is fairly certain a tornado will strike, it is still impossible to predict exactly where its path will hit. Certain precautions can be taken when a tornado is imminent, but there is no known way even to slightly influence the incredible power of the tornado once it has formed.

Avalanche control consists of mechanically inducing avalanches to fall before they have a chance to build up to mammoth proportions,

168

through the use of explosives, and, as a second line of defense, building walls around inhabited areas which, hopefully, will stop the cascading snow and debris. But again, in many cases the only possible defensive action is to evacuate threatened areas, which saves lives but can do little to save property.

There is obviously nothing that can be done to control an erupting volcano, and even the prediction of volcanic activity is extremely difficult and inexact.

Potential earthquake damage can be minimized with modern knowledge of earthquake-resistant building techniques, but even the most earthquake-proof building may fall if the epicenter of a large quake is near it. Again, the main preventive action which can save human life is evacuation, and in many cases this is totally impractical, since some tremendous cities, filled with millions of people have been built in earthquake zones. Many attempts have been made by seismologists to predict earthquakes, but for the most part they are unsatisfactory. One of the most impressive things about earthquakes is their total unexpectedness.

Extensive observation of American forests during the dry season, modern techniques of smoke jumping which put men on the spot while fires are still small and controllable, and a massive public campaign to reduce carelessness with fire in the nation's woodland have considerably reduced the destructive effects of forest fires, but a tremendous and valuable national resource had already been partially destroyed when these measures began to take effect.

The great challenge of the earth is a never-ending source of wonder as men attempt to penetrate the mysteries surrounding the tremendous natural forces at work above and beneath our world. Despite the almost miraculous abilities of new scientific tools such as radar, electron miroscopes, transistorized space meters and atomic power, men can still only stand in awe of those enormous forces which periodically engulf him. Any natural disaster is an occasion both humbling and awe-inspiring, and despite the terrible personal tragedies which inevitably occur, natural forces have a grandeur which continues to remind us of our relative position in the scheme of things.

Frank A. Perret witnessed an eruption of Vesuvius in 1906 and his description hints at the mystery of life on earth. He wrote that his strongest impression was "that of an infinite dignity in every manifestation of this stupendous releasing of energy. No words can describe the majesty of its unfolding."

BIBLIOGRAPHY

Atwater, Montgomery M. *The Avalanche Hunters.* Philadelphia: Macrae Smith Co., 1968.

Bixby, William. *Havoc: The Story of Natural Disasters.* New York: Longmans, Green and Co., 1961.

Corbett, Edmund V., ed. *Great True Stories of Tragedy and Disaster.* New York: Archer House, 1963.

Douglas, Marjory Stoneman. *Hurricane.* New York: Rinehart & Co., 1958.

Downey, Fairfax. *Disaster Fighters.* New York: G. P. Putnam's Sons, 1938.

Dunn, Gordon E. and Banner I. Miller. *Atlantic Hurricanes.* Louisiana: State University Press, 1964.

Engle, Eloise. *Earthquake!* New York: The John Day Co., 1966.

Fraser, Colin. *The Avalanche Enigma.* New York: Rand McNally & Co., 1966.

Helm, Thomas. *Hurricanes: Weather at Its Worst.* New York: Dodd, Mead & Co., 1967.

Holbrook, Stewart H. *Burning an Empire.* New York: The Macmillan Co., 1943.

Hoyt, William G. and Walter B. Langbein. *Floods.* Princeton, New Jersey: Princeton University Press, 1955.

Hurst, Randle M. *The Smokejumpers.* Caldwell, Idaho: The Caxton Printers, 1966.

Lane, Frank W. *The Elements Rage.* New York: Chilton Books, 1965.

Neider, Charles, ed. *Man Against Nature.* New York: Harper & Bros., 1954.

Robinson, Donald. *The Face of Disaster.* Garden City, New York: Doubleday & Co., 1959.

Shepard, Francis P. *The Earth Beneath the Sea.* Baltimore, Md.: The Johns Hopkins Press, 1967.

Sloane, Eric. *Book of Storms.* New York: Duell, Sloan and Pearce, 1956.

Sutton, Ann and Myron. *Nature on the Rampage.* New York: J. B. Lippincott Co., 1962.

Tannehill, Ivan Ray. *Hurricanes: Their Nature and History.* Princeton, New Jersey: Princeton University Press, 1938.

Werstein, Irving. *The Blizzard of '88.* New York: Thomas Y. Crowell Co., 1960.

Wilcoxson, Kent H. *Chains of Fire: The Story of Volcanoes.* New York: Chilton Books, 1966.

Wolfenstein, Martha. *Disaster: A Psychological Essay.* Glenco, Illinois: The Free Press, 1957.

INDEX

in Chile, 164-165; in
China, 8; effects of, 135;
in Europe, 123, 126;
evacuation during, 169;
in Japan, 120-123, 165;
losses from, 8, 120-136;
prediction of, 169; in
seismic belts, 134
Elements Rage, The, 11,
69, 88
Ervin, Balas, 130

Flash floods, characteristics of, 79
Floods,
in Asia, 81; characteris-
tics of, 78-80; in China,
82; destruction during,
68-72; in East Pakistan,
81; effective control of,
168; in England, 68, 69,
74, 75; in Holland, 74-
78; by inland water
overflow, 78, 79; losses
from, 8, 68-83; in Lower
Mississippi area, 80, 81;
in North America, 80;
in Pennsylvania, 71, 72;
prevention of potential
damage, 83; rainfall
during, 69, 70; types of,
73, 74, 78; in Utah, 79
Floyd, Tom, 68, 69
Forest fires,
losses from, 102-119;
methods of control, 118;
in Montana, 118; pre-
ventive action against,
169; statistics on, 112,

113; use of smoke jump-
ers, 118, 169; in Oregon,
113-118; in Wisconsin,
104-113
Fuller, Norma, 46

Geothermal heat, as source
of energy, 10
Golay, Christian, 94
Gray, R.W., 66
*Great True Stories of
Tragedy and Disaster*,
105
Gross, Burtel, 94, 95

Hain, Frank, 25
Harpum, John, 11
Hartford, 20
Hartman, Stephen, 91, 92
Heilprin, Angelo, 149
Housel, 159, 160
Hurricane Audrey, 63-66
Hurricane Carol, 51-55
Hurricane Dolly, 54
Hurricane Edna, 54-56
Hurricane Hazel, 55-57, 66
Hurricanes, aftermath of,
66; characteristics of,
57, 58; destruction by,
59-62; forecasting of,
168; at Guadeloupe, 60;
rising tide during, 62,
63; in Puerto Rico, 60;
at St. Thomas, 59; in
Texas, 62, 63; in Toron-
to, 62; torrential rains
during, 62; wind veloci-
ty of, 58, 59

Shepard, Francis, family, 155-157

Taylor, Bill, 131
Temperate Zone storms, characteristics of, 58
Theuss, Stephen, 98
Thomas Crawford, 20
Thut, Ernst, 96
Tidal Waves, losses from, 29, 155-170
Toner, Peter J., 71
Tornadoes,
    advance warning of, 48, 168; in Alabama, 47; average occurrence of, 47; in the Carolinas, 47; characteristics of, 33; forces of, 35; in Illinois, 36, 47; in Indiana, 47; in Kansas, 36, 40, 41; in Kentucky, 47; losses from, 8, 31-48; in Massachusetts, 43-47; in Missouri, 47; in Oklahoma, 42; states most frequently hit, 34; in Tennessee, 47; in Texas, 36-42; typical weather of, 34
Towle, Samuel, 25
Tsunami (giant waves), characteristics of, 126, 132; in Chile, 164, 165; in Hawaiian Islands, 151-160, 165; in Japan, 165, 166; speed of, 160
Typhoons, characteristics

of, 58; losses from, 9, 10

Unold, Eugene, 93, 94

Volcanoes, Hawaiian eruptions, 151; Icelandic eruptions, 151; Krakatoa eruption, 9, 11, 160-162; losses from, 8, 9, 137-154; Peléan eruption, 153; prediction of eruption, 169; stages of, 150, 151; Strombolian eruptions, 152; Vulcanian eruptions, 152, 153

Wait, James J., 32
Wallace, Gordon L. family, 133, 134
Waterspout, effects of, 32, 33
Wilson, Sara, 15, 21
Woolley, Sir Leonard, 81

Yates, Ken, 129